EASY PIANO

CHART HITS
OF 2016–2017

ISBN 978-1-4950-9293-0

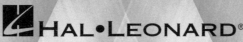

7777 W. BLUEMOUND RD. P.O. BOX 13819 MILWAUKEE, WI 53213

Visit Hal Leonard Online at
www.halleonard.com

CONTENTS

3 **CAKE BY THE OCEAN**
DNCE

8 **CLOSER**
The Chainsmokers featuring Halsey

14 **COLD WATER**
Major Lazer
featuring Justin Bieber and MØ

18 **DON'T LET ME DOWN**
The Chainsmokers featuring Daya

25 **DON'T WANNA KNOW**
Maroon 5 featuring Kendrick Lamar

32 **HEATHENS**
twenty one pilots

42 **HUMAN**
Rag 'n' Bone Man

48 **I DON'T WANNA
LIVE FOREVER
(FIFTY SHADES DARKER)**
ZAYN and Taylor Swift

37 **LET ME LOVE YOU**
DJ Snake featuring Justin Bieber

54 **LOVE YOURSELF**
Justin Bieber

60 **LUSH LIFE**
Zara Larsson

66 **PERFECT STRANGERS**
Jonas Blue featuring JP Cooper

71 **ROCKABYE**
Clean Bandit featuring Sean Paul

80 **SAY YOU WON'T LET GO**
James Arthur

84 **SIDE TO SIDE**
Ariana Grande featuring Nicki Minaj

90 **STARBOY**
The Weeknd featuring Daft Punk

96 **THIS TOWN**
Niall Horan

101 **TREAT YOU BETTER**
Shawn Mendes

108 **24K MAGIC**
Bruno Mars

115 **WORK FROM HOME**
Fifty Harmony featuring Ty Dolla $ign

CAKE BY THE OCEAN

Words and Music by JOSEPH JONAS,
JUSTIN TRANTER, ROBIN FREDRIKSSON
and MATTIAS LARSSON

Driving Dance beat

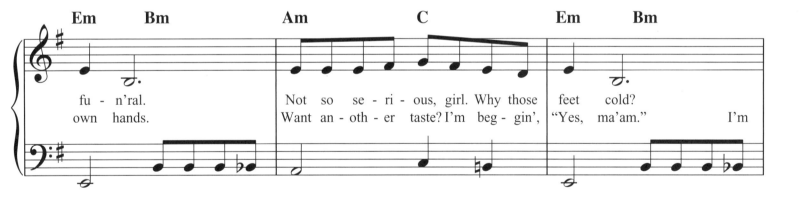

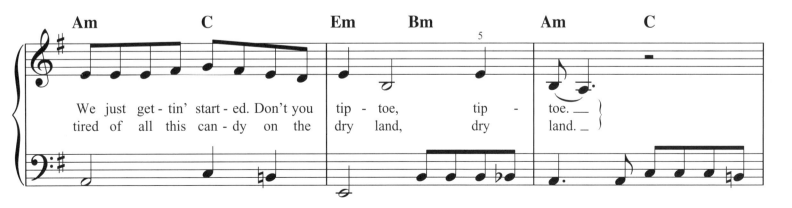

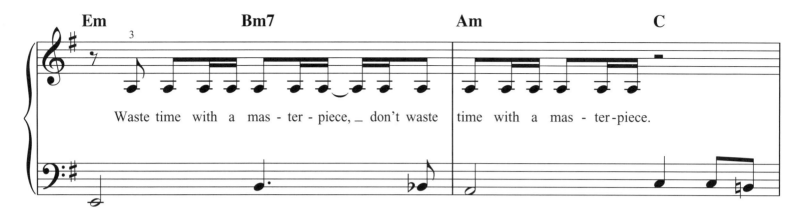

Waste time with a mas-ter-piece, __ don't waste time with a mas-ter-piece.

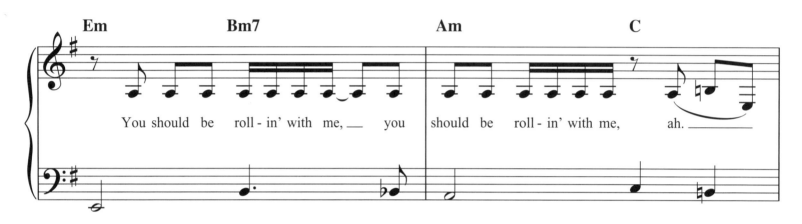

You should be roll-in' with me, ___ you should be roll-in' with me, ah. ___

You're a real-life fan-ta-sy, ___ you're a real-life fan-ta-sy.

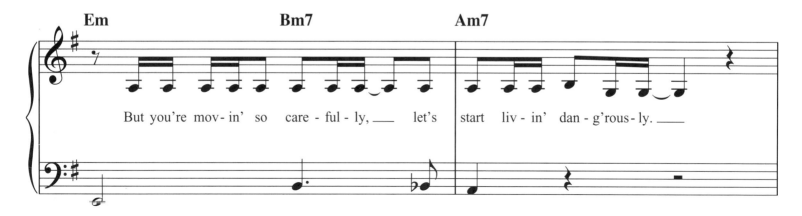

But you're mov-in' so care-ful-ly, ___ let's start liv-in' dan-g'rous-ly. ___

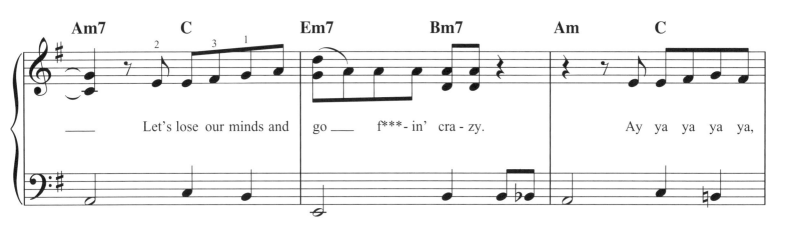

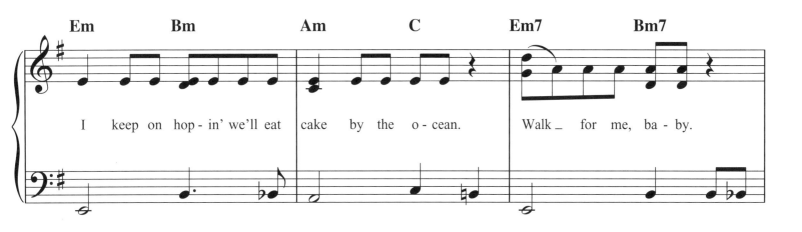

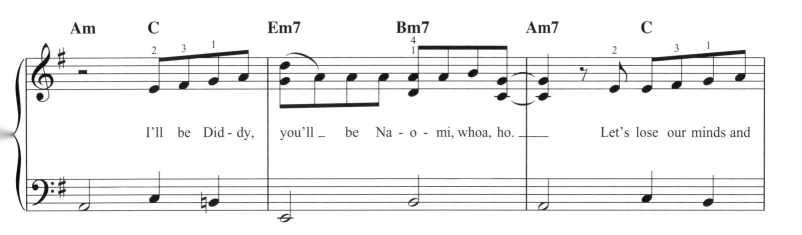

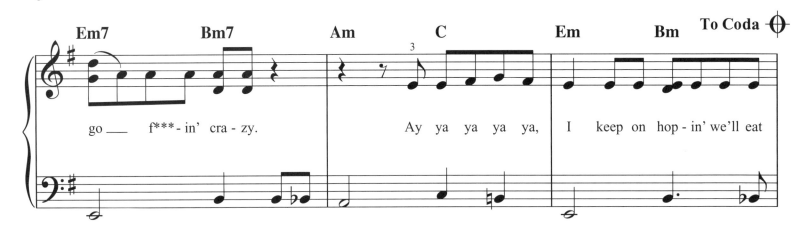

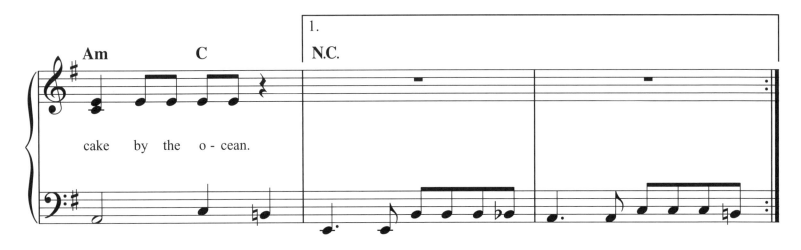

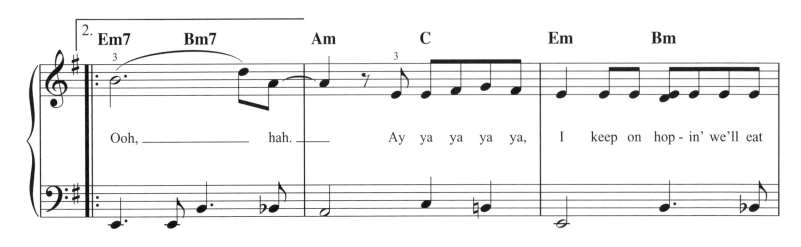

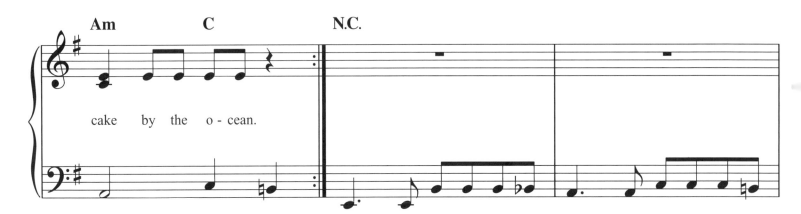

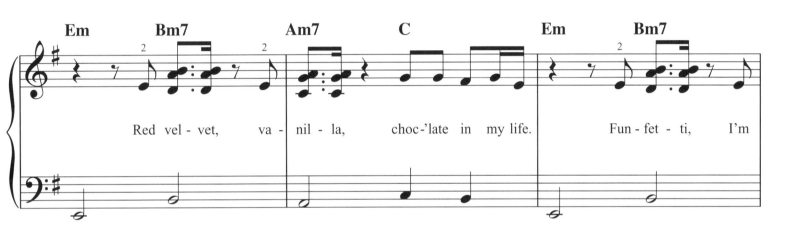

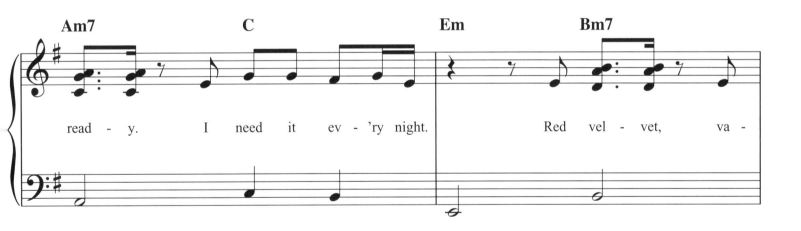

CLOSER

Words and Music by ANDREW TAGGART, ISAAC SLADE,
JOSEPH KING, ASHLEY FRANGIPANE, SHAUN FRANK
and FREDERIC KENNETT

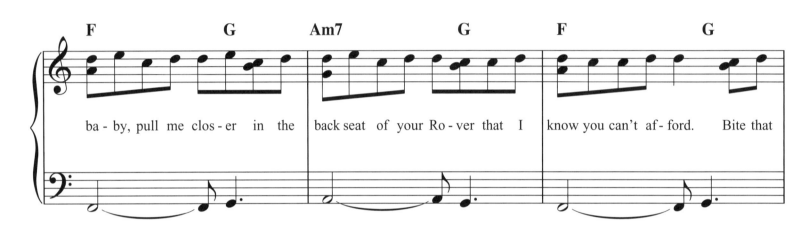

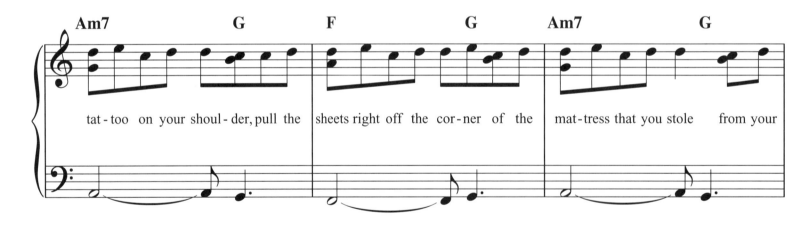

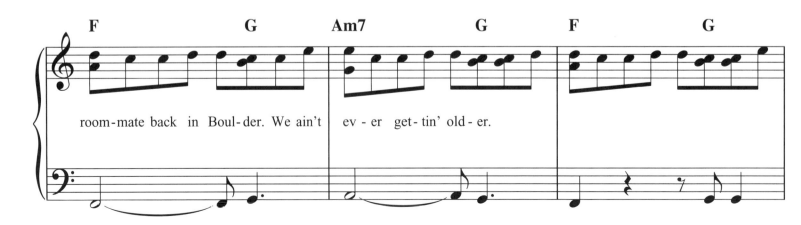

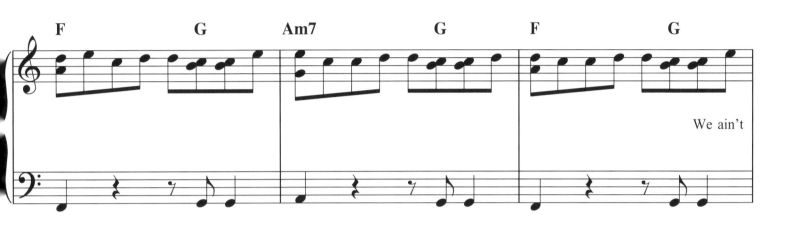

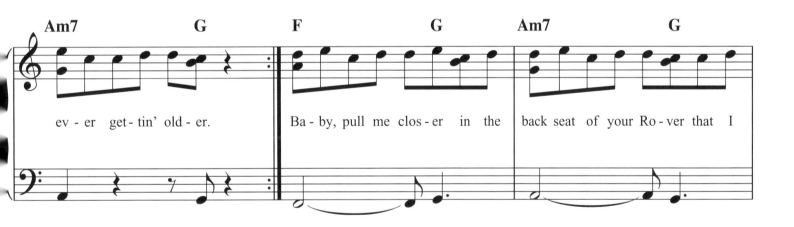

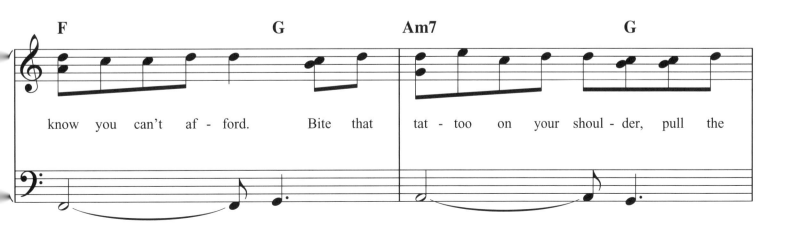

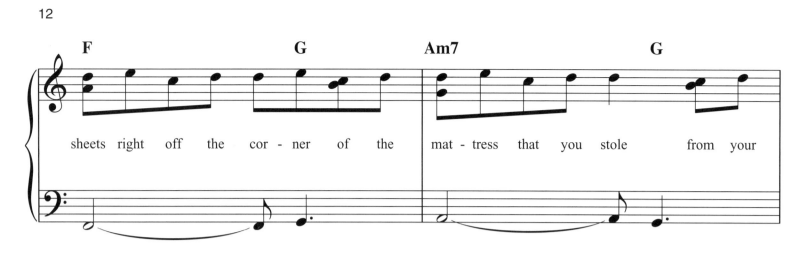

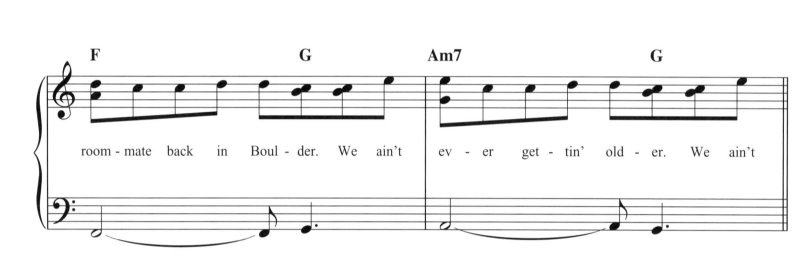

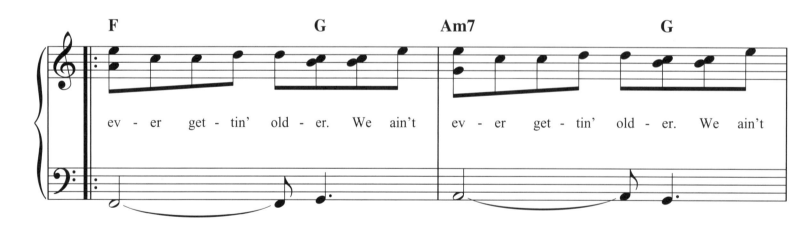

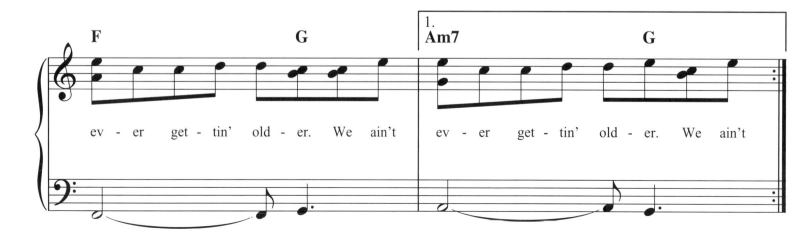

COLD WATER

Words and Music by THOMAS PENTZ,
KAREN ØRSTED, HENRY ALLEN, JUSTIN BIEBER,
BENJAMIN LEVIN, ED SHEERAN, JAMIE SCOTT
and PHILIP MECKSEPER

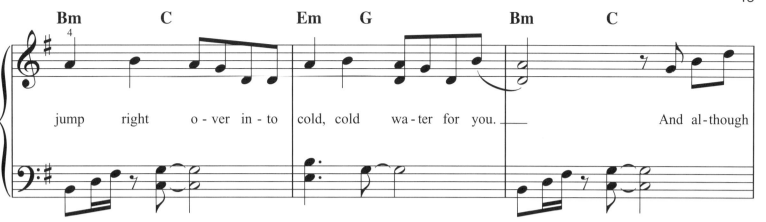

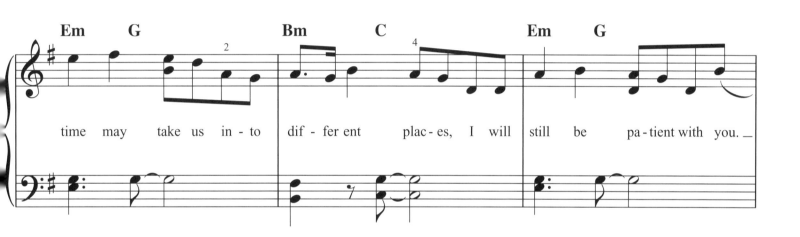

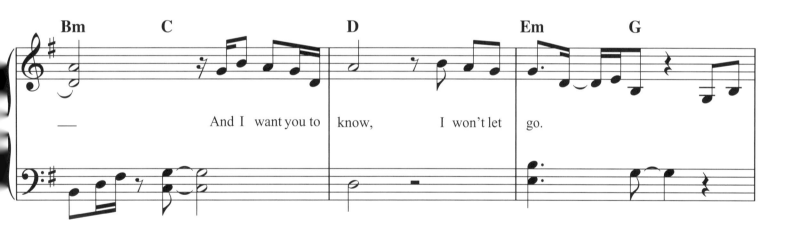

go.　　　　　　　　　　I'll be your life - line ___ to - night. _

___　　　　Come on, come on,　save me from my rock - ing boat.　I just wan - na stay a-

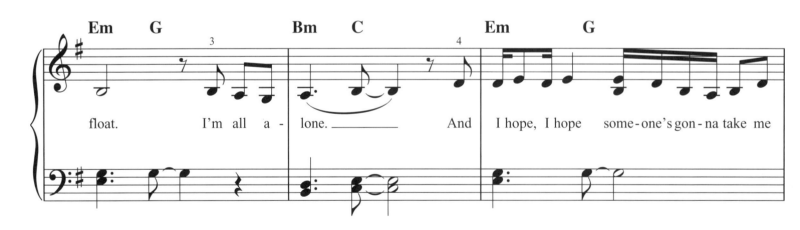

float.　I'm all a - lone. _____ And　I hope, I hope　some - one's gon - na take me

home,　some - where I can rest my soul.　I need to know ___ you won't let

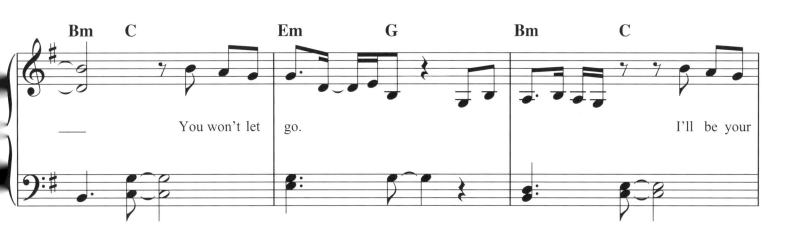

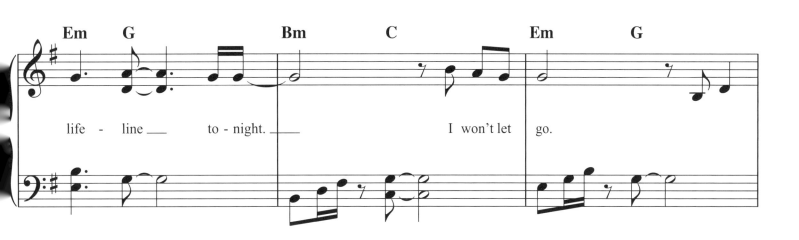

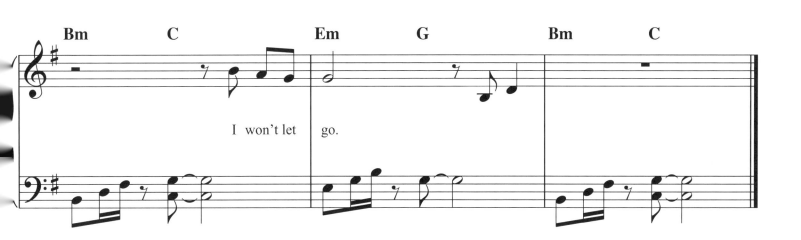

DON'T LET ME DOWN

Words and Music by ANDREW TAGGART,
EMILY SCHWARTZ and SCOTT HARRIS

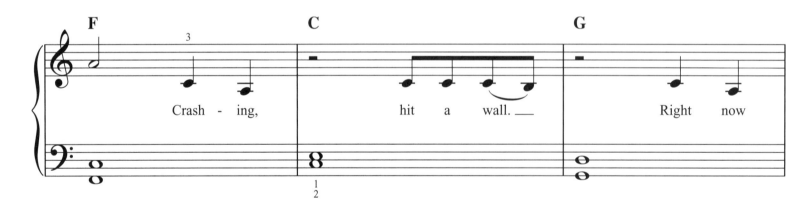

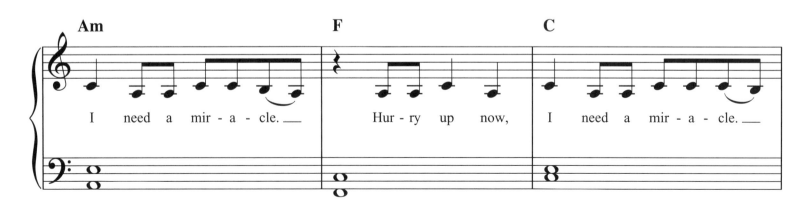

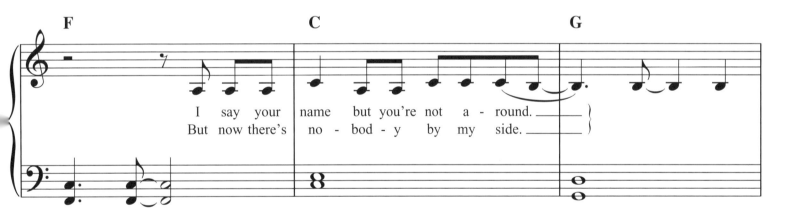

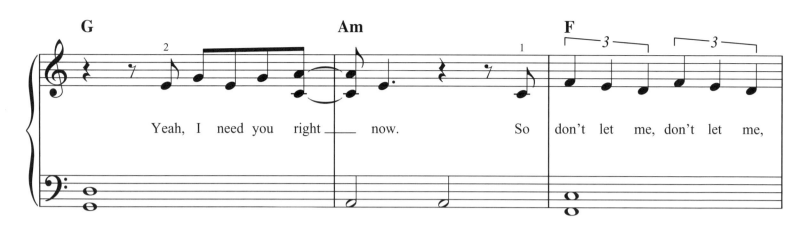

Yeah, I need you right ___ now. So don't let me, don't let me,

don't let me down. I think I'm los - ing my mind, ___ now. It's in my

head, dar - ling, I hope that you'll be here when I need you the

most. ___ So don't let me, don't let me, don't let me down.

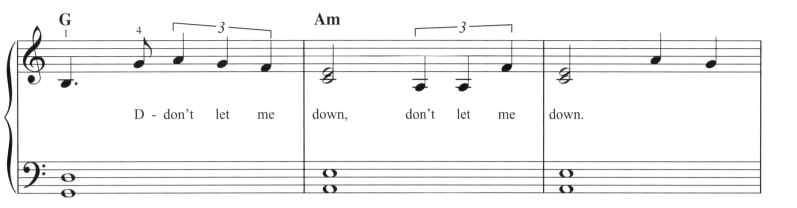

D - don't let me down, don't let me down.

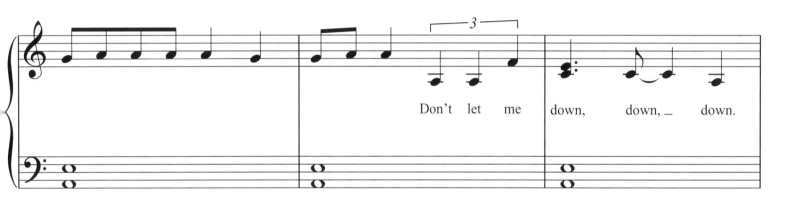

Don't let me down, down,_ down.

Don't let me down, don't let me

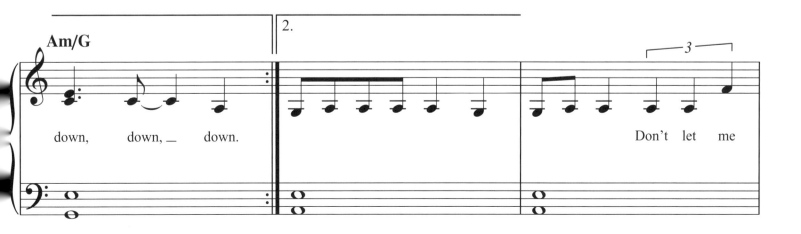

down, down,_ down. Don't let me

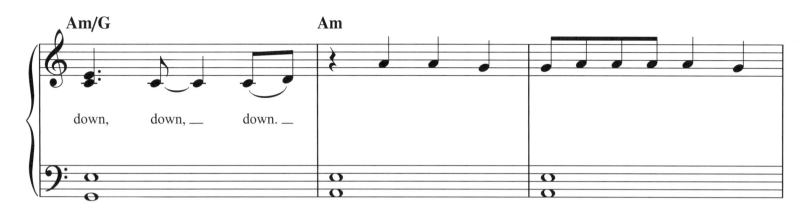

down,   down, __   down. __

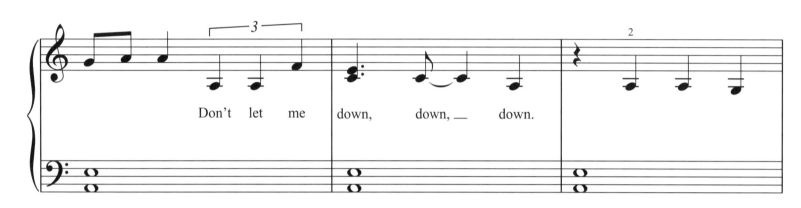

Don't let me   down,   down, __   down.

Don't let me   down,   Don't let me   down,   down, __   down.

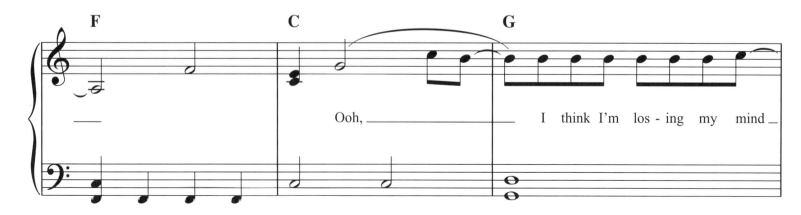

__   Ooh, _____   I think I'm los-ing my mind __

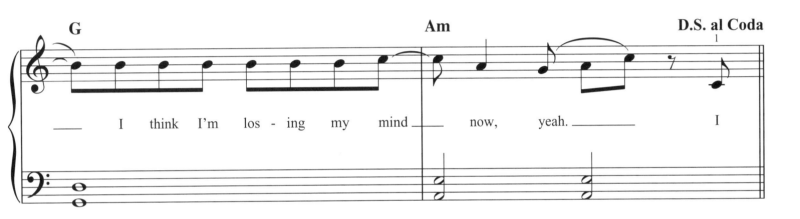

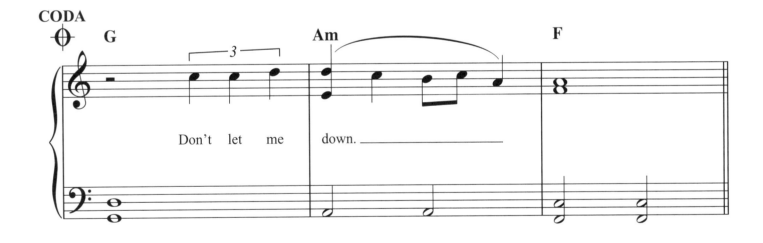

24

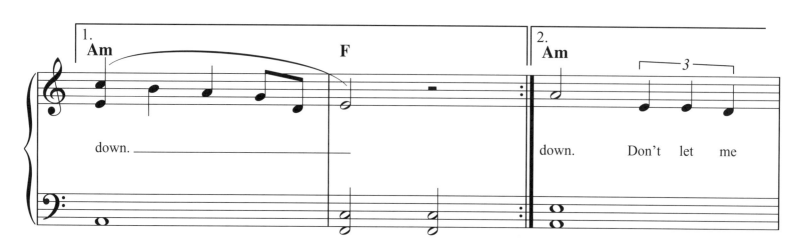

DON'T WANNA KNOW

Words and Music by ADAM LEVINE, BENJAMIN LEVIN,
JOHN HENRY RYAN, AMMAR MALIK, JACOB KASHER HINDLIN,
ALEX BEN-ABDALLAH, KENDRICK LAMAR, KURTIS McKENZIE
and JON MILLS

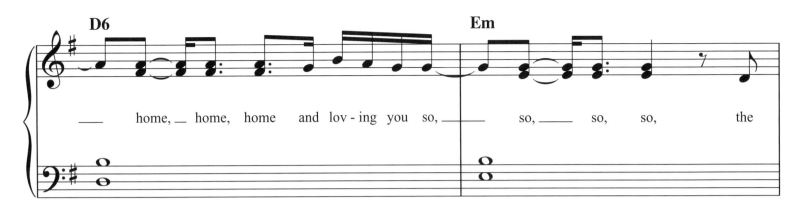

home, home, home and lov-ing you so, __ so, __ so, so, the

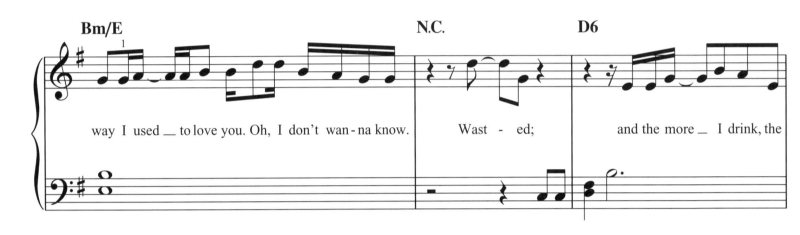

way I used __ to love you. Oh, I don't wan-na know. Wast - ed; and the more __ I drink, the

more I think a-bout __ you. Oh no, no, __ I can't take __ it.

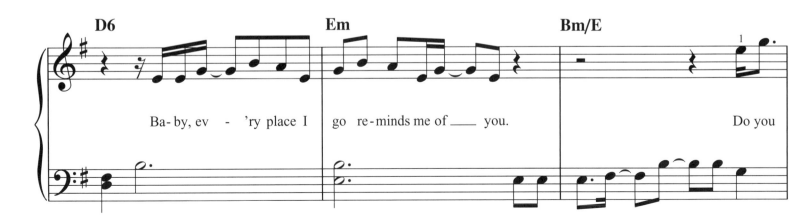

Ba- by, ev - 'ry place I go re-minds me of __ you. Do you

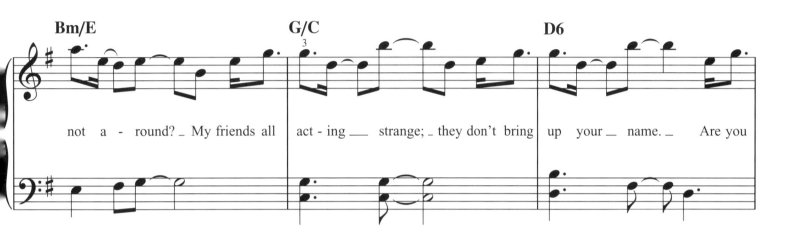

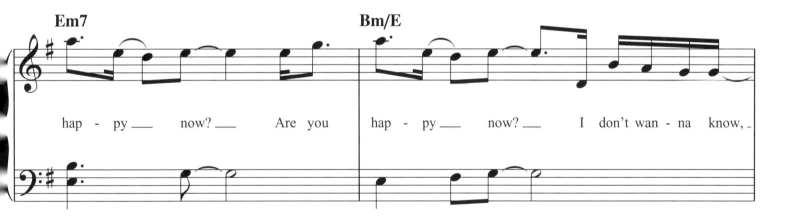

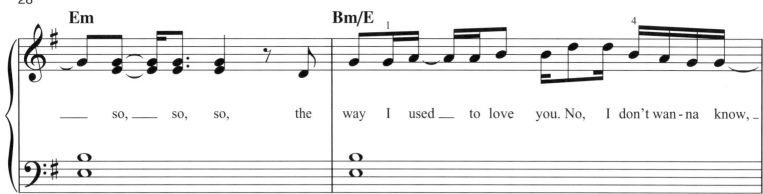

so, so, so, the way I used to love you. No, I don't wan-na know,

know, know, know who's tak-ing you home, home, home, home and lov-ing you so,

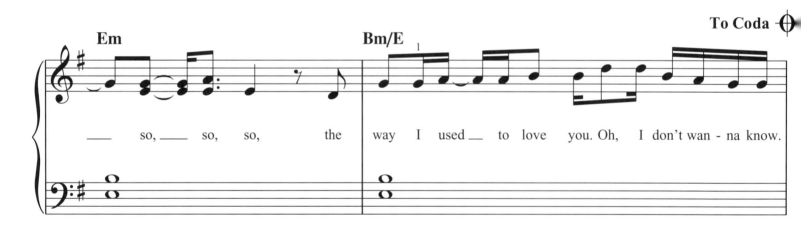

To Coda ⊕

so, so, so, the way I used to love you. Oh, I don't wan-na know.

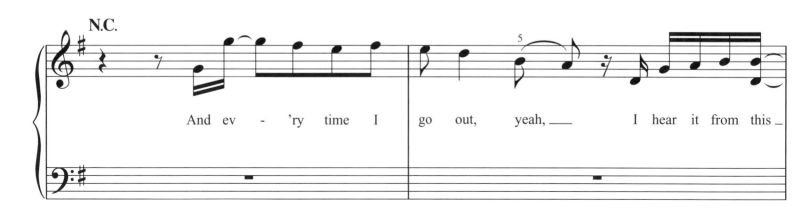

And ev - 'ry time I go out, yeah, I hear it from this

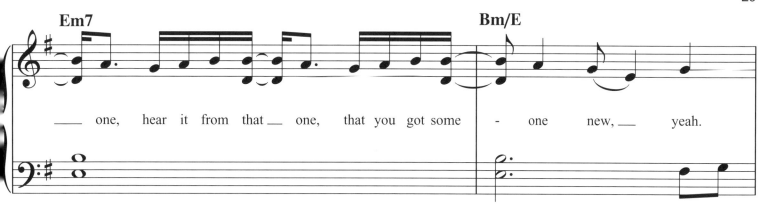

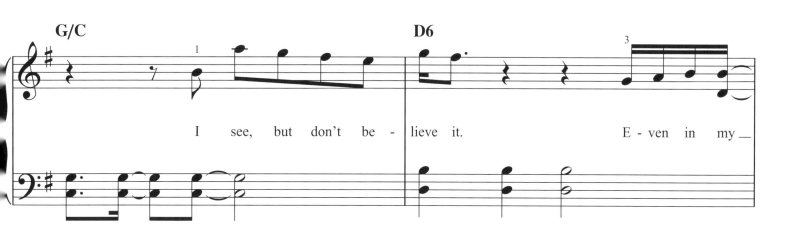

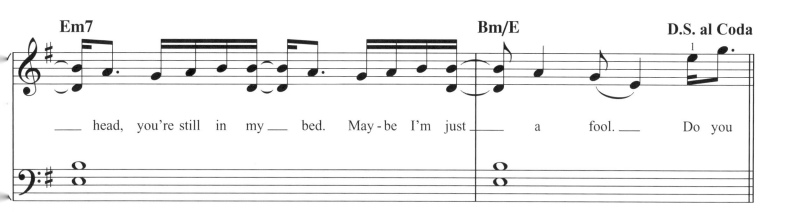

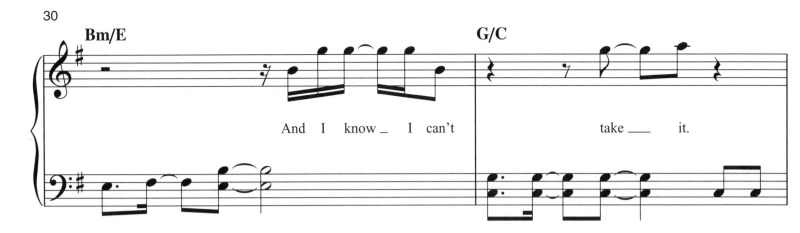

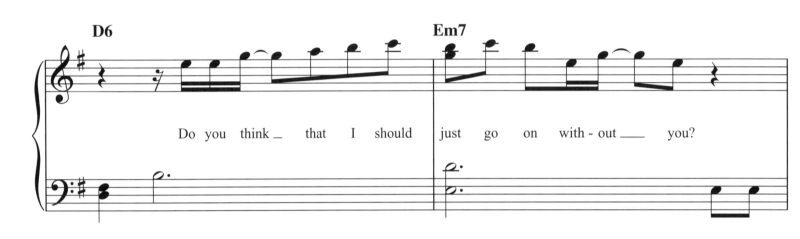

HEATHENS
from SUICIDE SQUAD

Words and Music by
TYLER JOSEPH

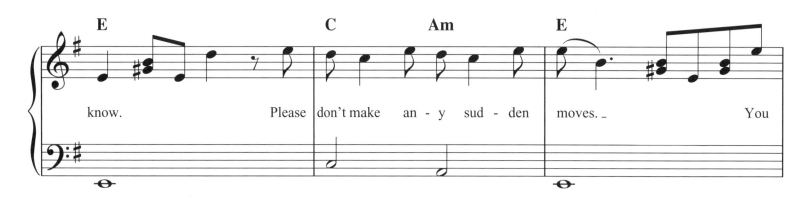

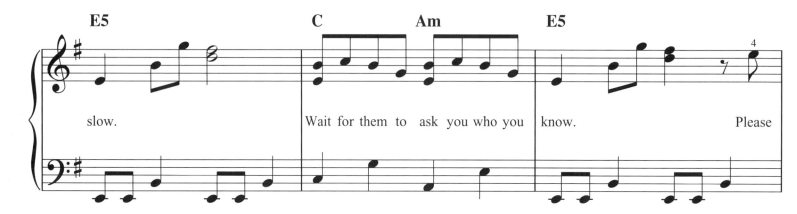

To Coda ⊕

don't make an-y sud-den moves. __ You don't know the half of the a - buse. __

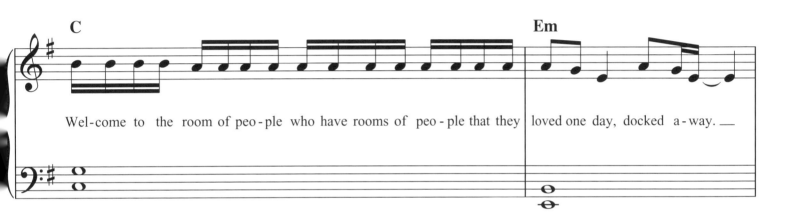

Wel-come to the room of peo-ple who have rooms of peo-ple that they loved one day, docked a-way. __

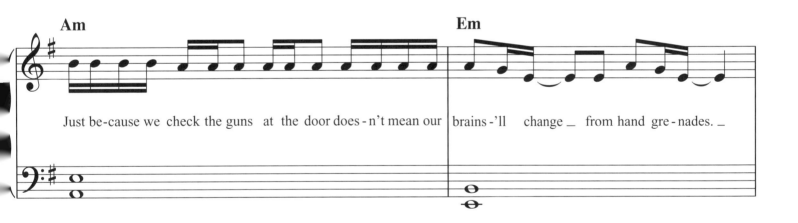

Just be-cause we check the guns at the door does-n't mean our brains-'ll change __ from hand gre-nades. __

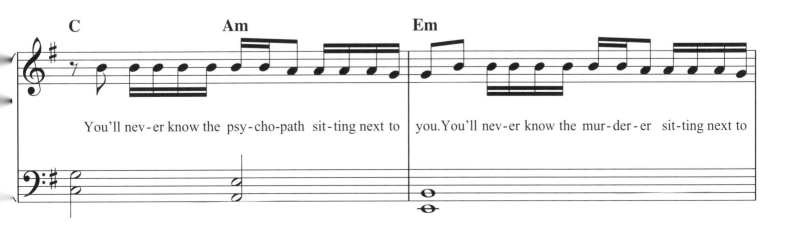

You'll nev-er know the psy-cho-path sit-ting next to you. You'll nev-er know the mur-der-er sit-ting next to

You. You'll think, "How'd I get here, sit-ting next to you?" But af-ter all I've said, please don't for - get.

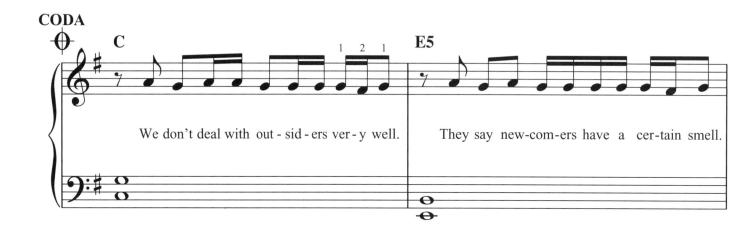

We don't deal with out - sid - ers ver - y well. They say new-com-ers have a cer-tain smell.

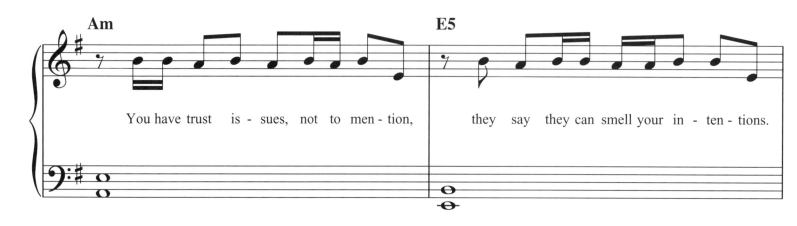

You have trust is - sues, not to men - tion, they say they can smell your in - ten - tions.

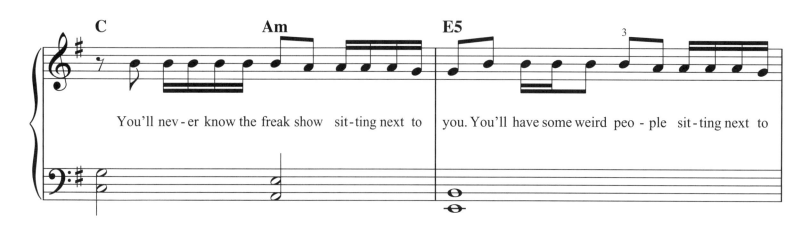

You'll nev - er know the freak show sit-ting next to you. You'll have some weird peo - ple sit-ting next to

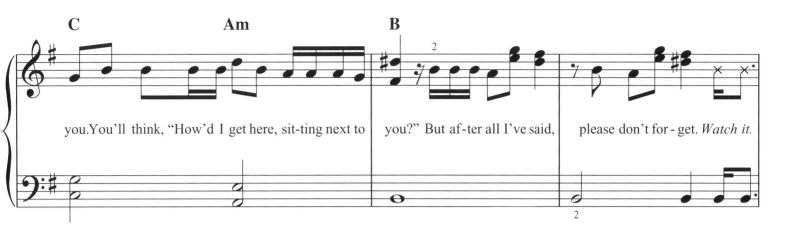

you.You'll think, "How'd I get here, sit-ting next to you?" But af-ter all I've said, please don't for-get. *Watch it.*

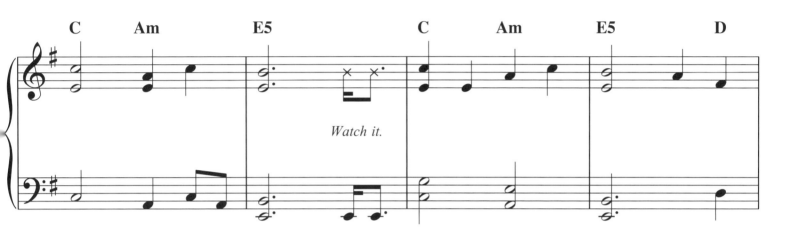

Watch it.

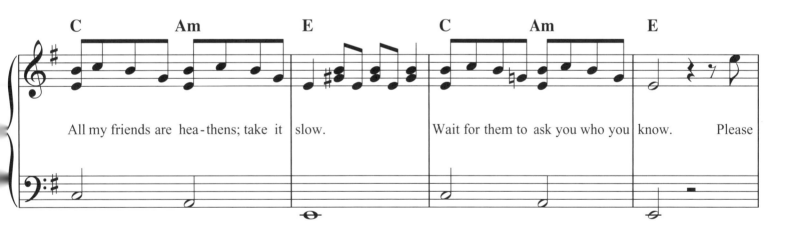

All my friends are hea-thens; take it slow. Wait for them to ask you who you know. Please

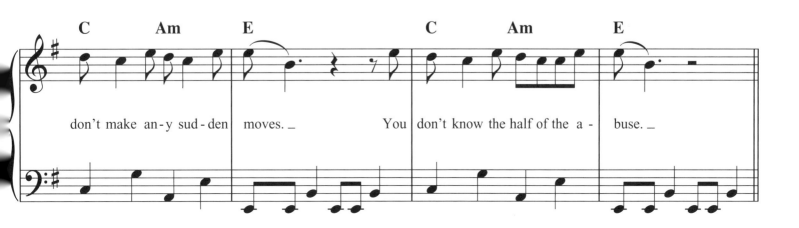

don't make an-y sud-den moves. _ You don't know the half of the a- buse. _

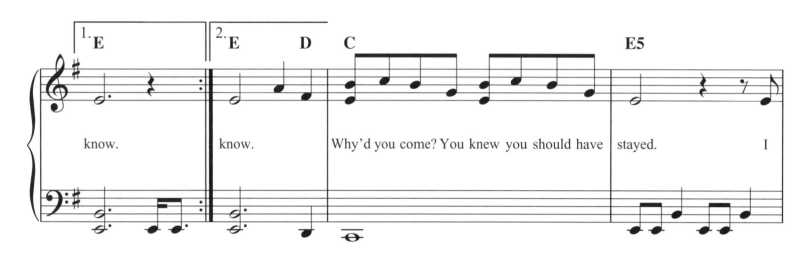

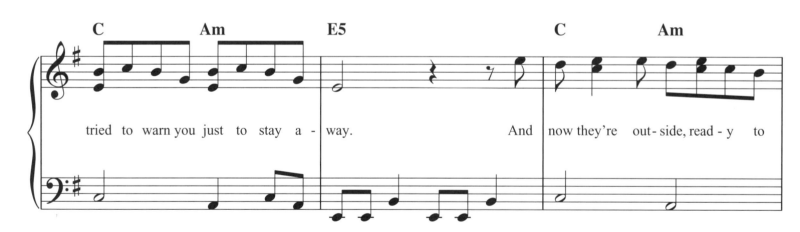

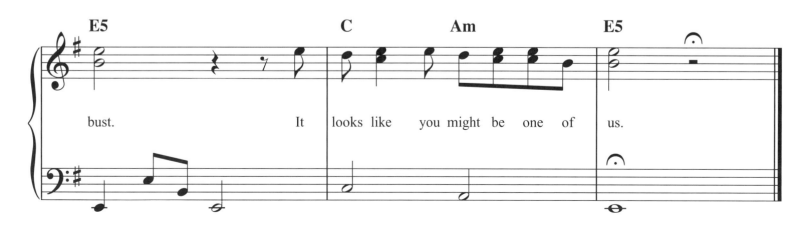

LET ME LOVE YOU

Words and Music by JUSTIN BIEBER, CARL ROSEN,
WILLIAM GRIGAHCINE, EDWIN PEREZ, TEDDY MENDEZ,
ANDREW WOTMAN, ALEXANDRA TAMPOSI, LOUIS BELL,
LUMIDEE CEDENO, BRIAN LEE and STEVEN MARSDEN

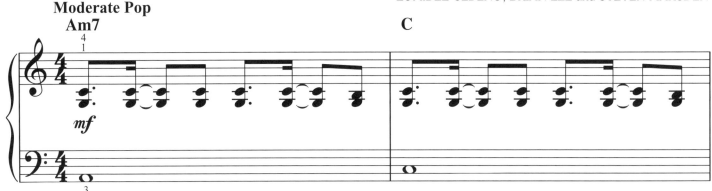

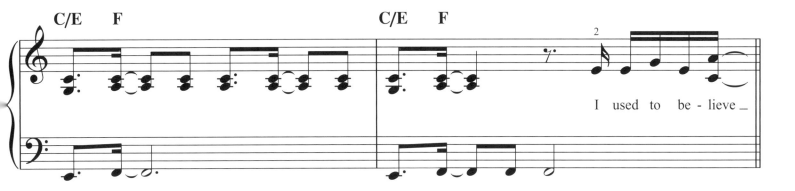

I used to be-lieve

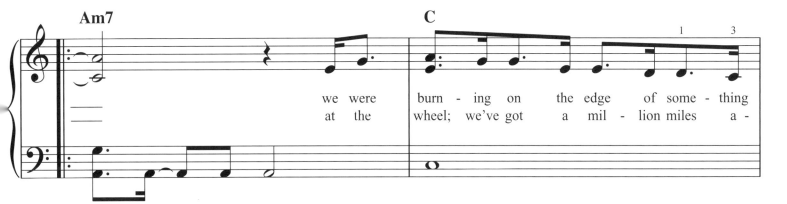

we were / at the   burn-ing on / wheel; we've got   the edge / a mil-   of some- / lion miles   thing / a-

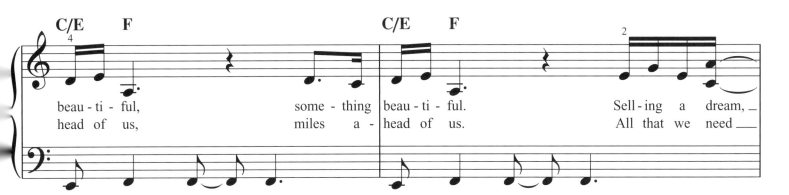

beau-ti-ful, / head of us,   some-thing / miles a-   beau-ti-ful. / head of us.   Sell-ing a dream, / All that we need

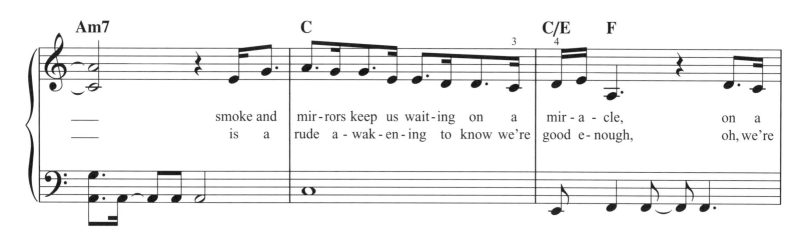

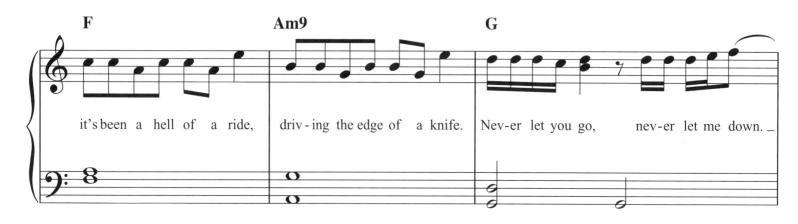

Don't fall a - sleep

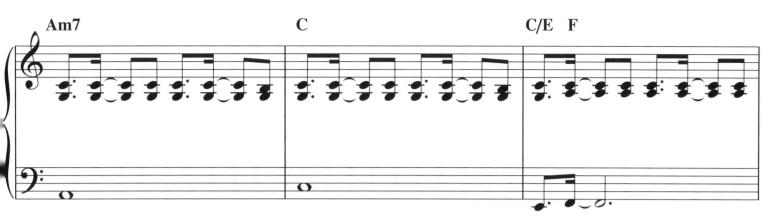

Don't you give up, ___ na, ___ na, na. I won't give up, ___ na, ___ na, na. Let ___ me

love you, ___ let ___ me love you. ___ Don't you give up, ___ na, ___ na, na. I won't give up, ___

___ na, ___ na, na. Let ___ me love you, ___ let ___ me love you. ___

HUMAN

Words and Music by JAMIE HARTMAN
and RORY GRAHAM

Moderately slow

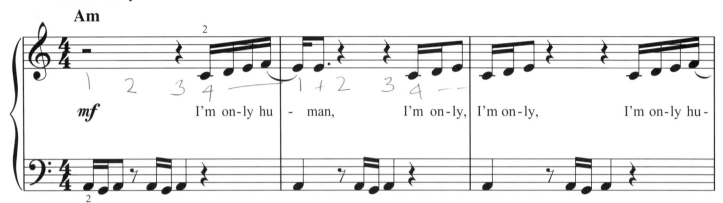

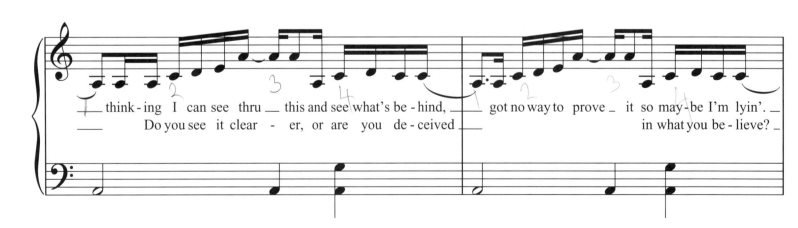

3/5/18
Both hands
with rhythm

some peo-ple think I can solve them, __ Lord heav-ens a - bove. __ I'm on-ly hu-

FACE

- man af-ter all, __ I'm on-ly hu - man af-ter all, __ don't put the blame __ on __

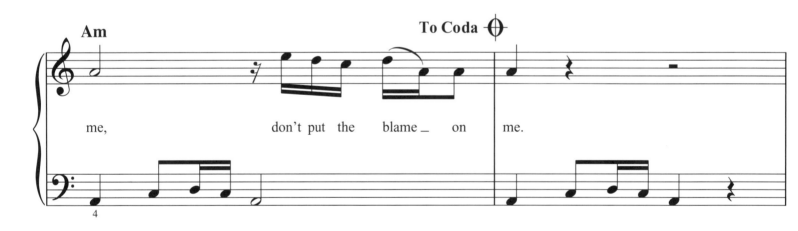

me, don't put the blame __ on me.

Don't ask my o-pin - ion, don't ask me to lie __ then beg for for-give - ness for mak-ing you cry, __

for mak-ing you cry. _____ 'Cause I'm on - ly hu -

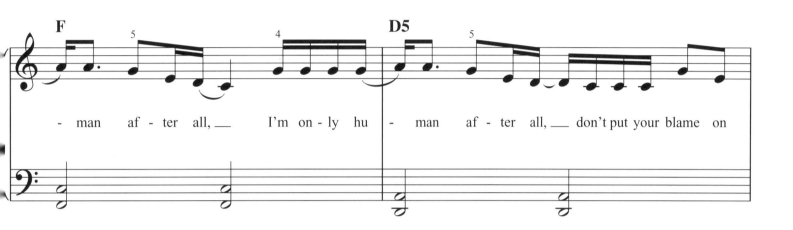

- man af - ter all, ___ I'm on - ly hu - man af - ter all, ___ don't put your blame on

me, _____ don't put the blame _ on ___ me.

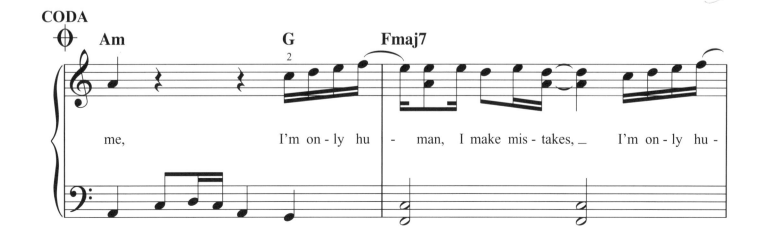

me, _____ I'm on - ly hu - man, I make mis - takes, _ I'm on - ly hu -

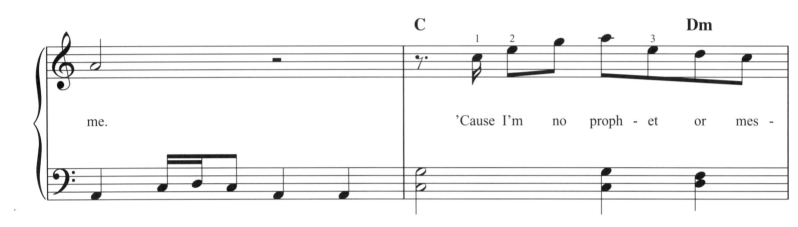

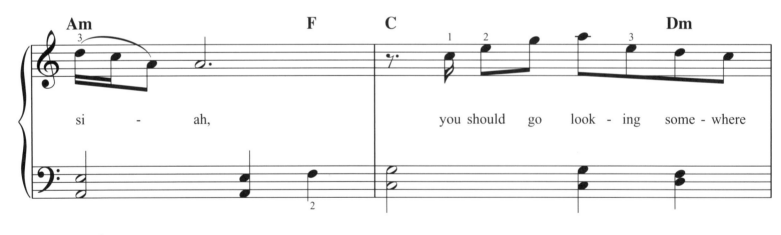

G# B E

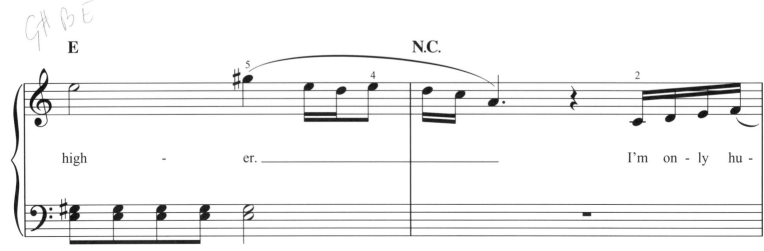

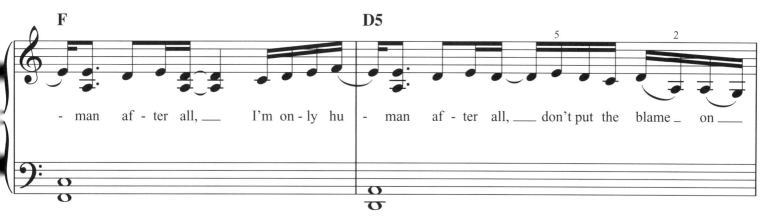

I DON'T WANNA LIVE FOREVER

(Fifty Shades Darker)

from FIFTY SHADES DARKER

Words and Music by TAYLOR SWIFT,
JACK ANTONOFF and SAM DEW

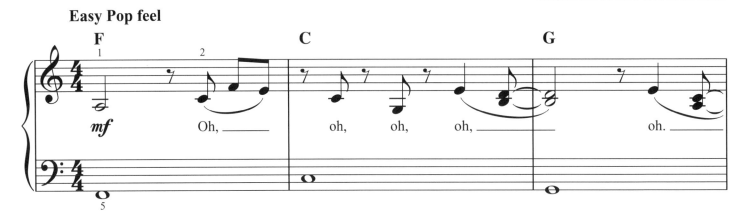

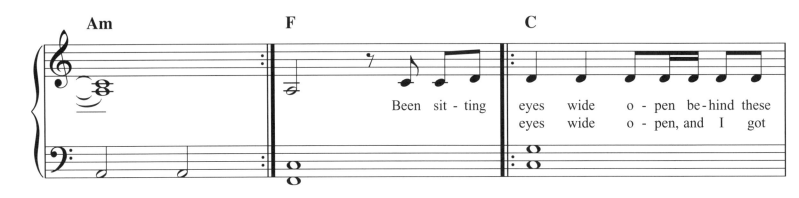

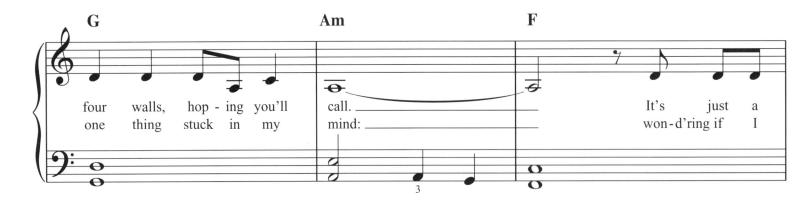

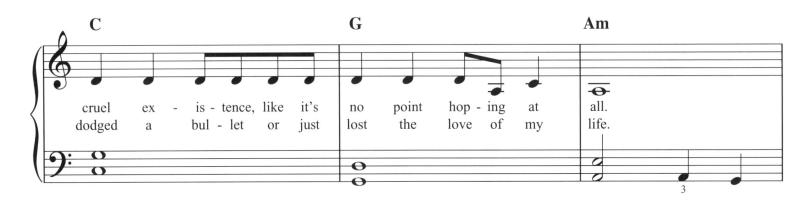

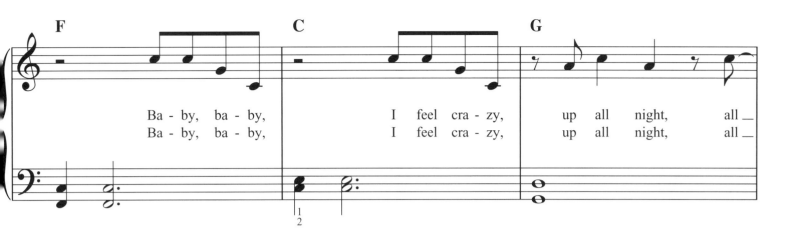

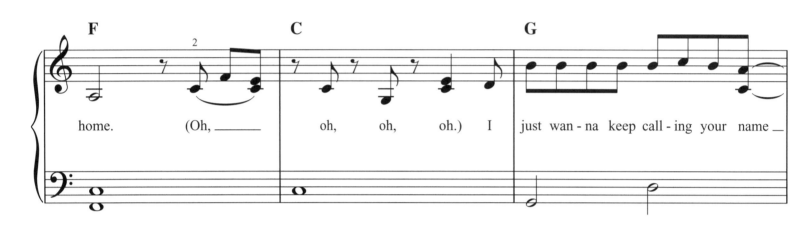

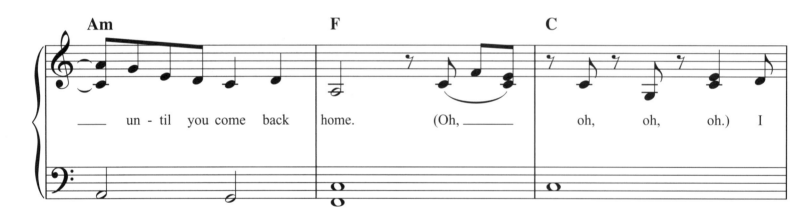

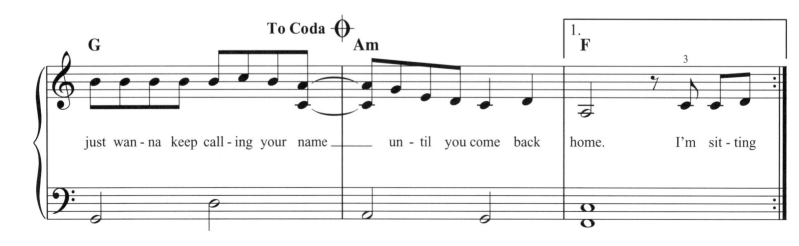

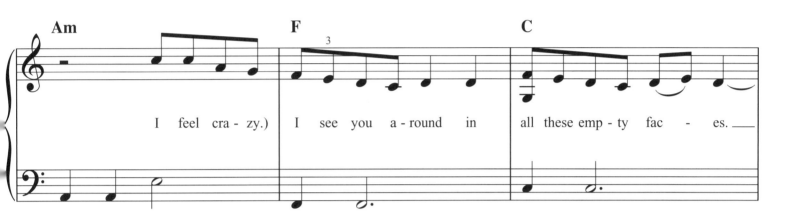

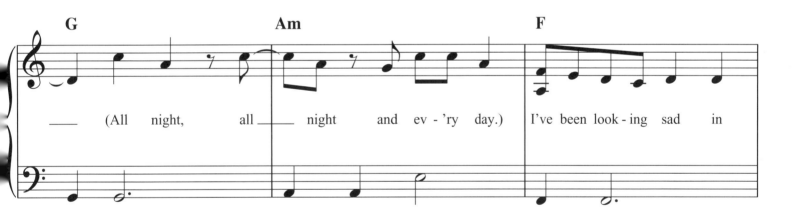

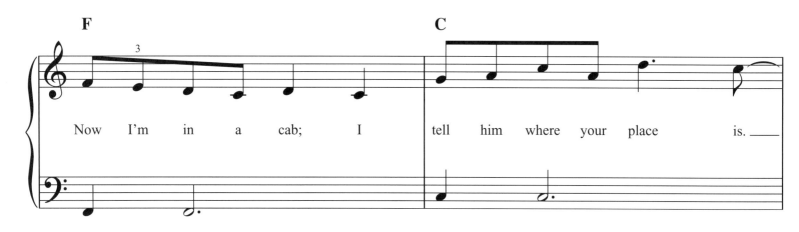

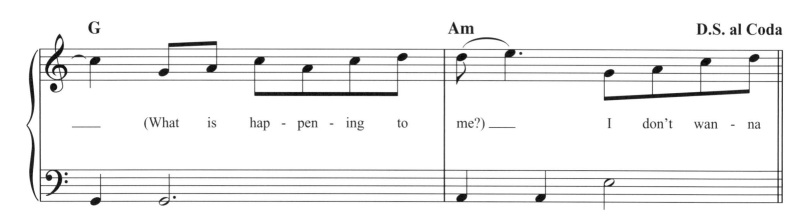

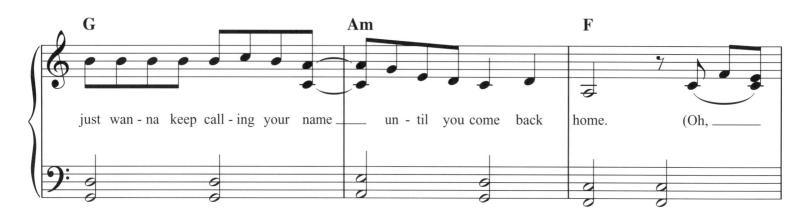

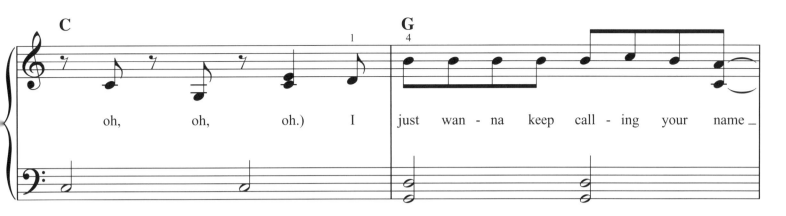

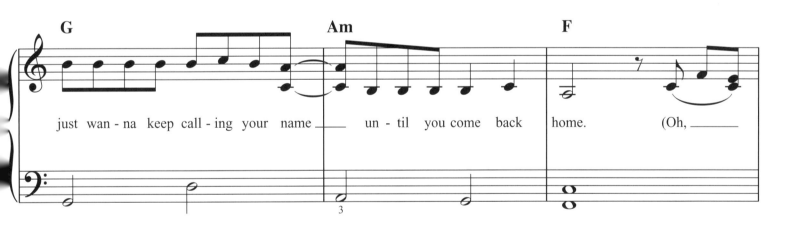

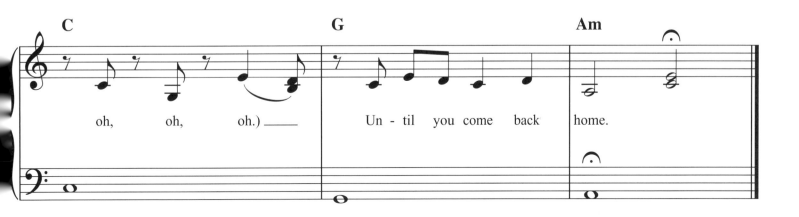

LOVE YOURSELF

Words and Music by JUSTIN BIEBER,
BENJAMIN LEVIN and ED SHEERAN

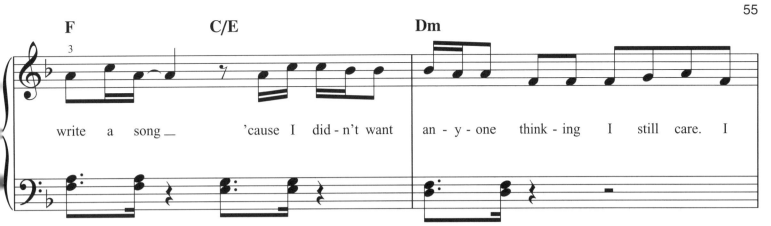

write a song — 'cause I did - n't want | an - y - one think - ing I still care. I

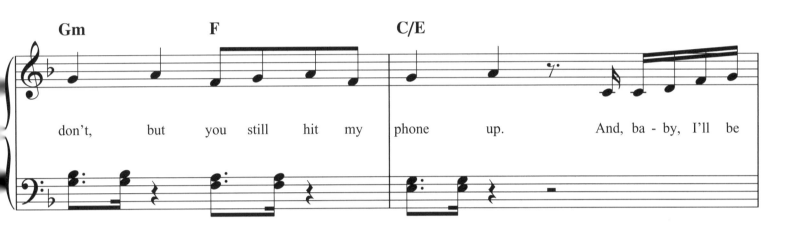

don't, but you still hit my | phone up. And, ba - by, I'll be

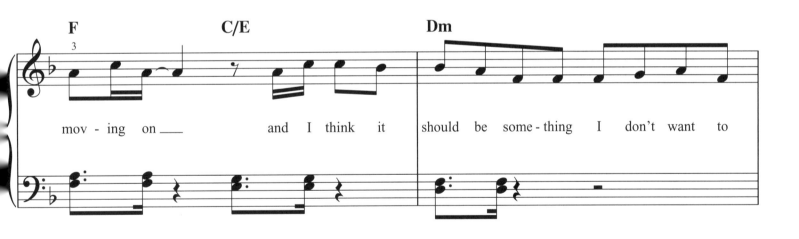

mov - ing on — and I think it | should be some - thing I don't want to

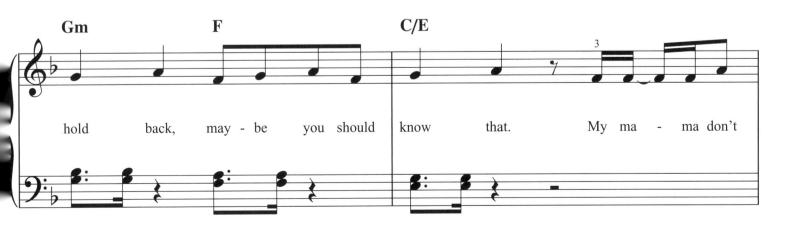

hold back, may - be you should | know that. My ma - ma don't

like you and she likes ev-e-ry-one. And I ____ nev-er

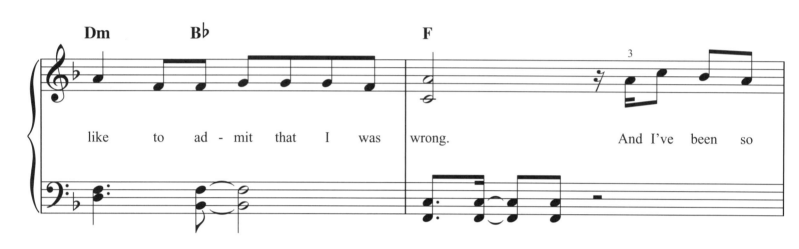

like to ad-mit that I was wrong. And I've been so

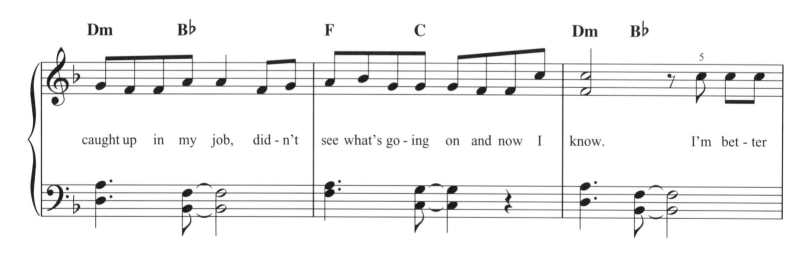

caught up in my job, did-n't see what's go-ing on and now I know. I'm bet-ter

sleep-ing on my own. 'Cause if you like the ___ way you look that ___ much, ___ oh ba-by,

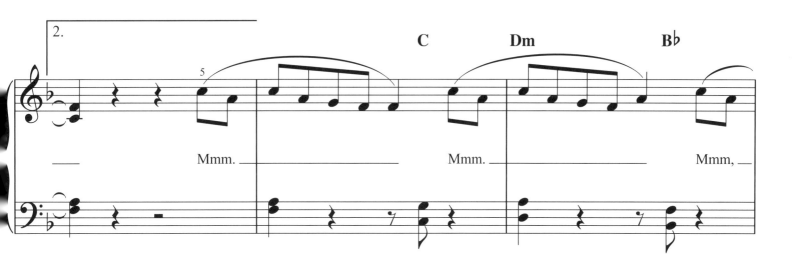

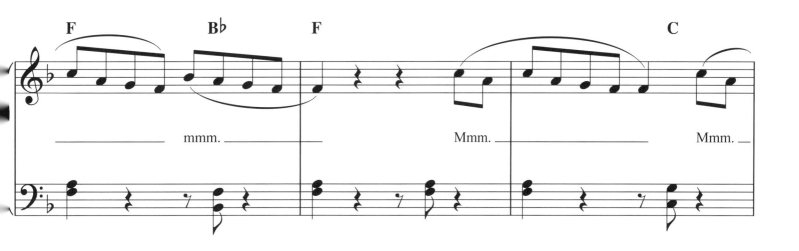

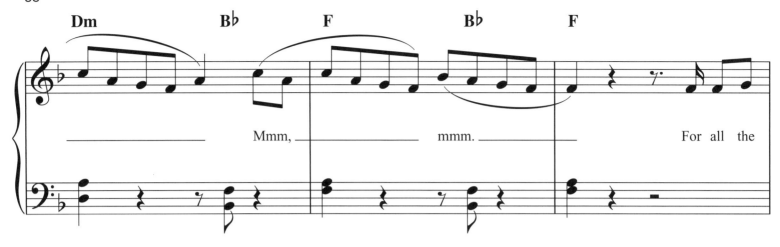

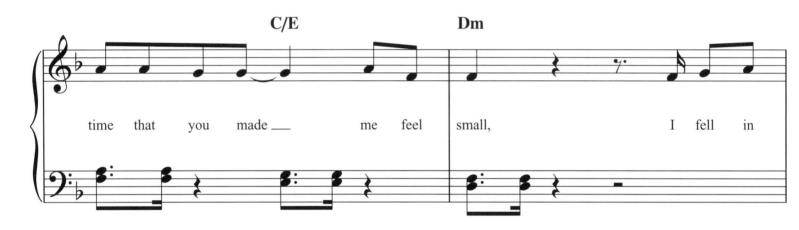

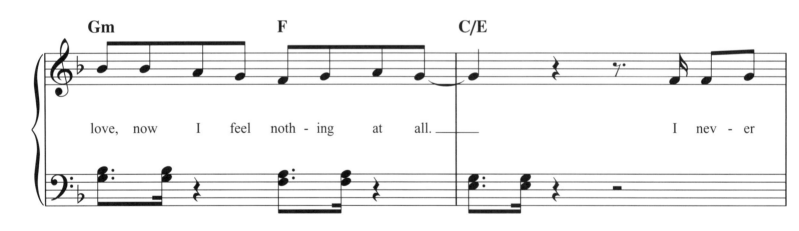

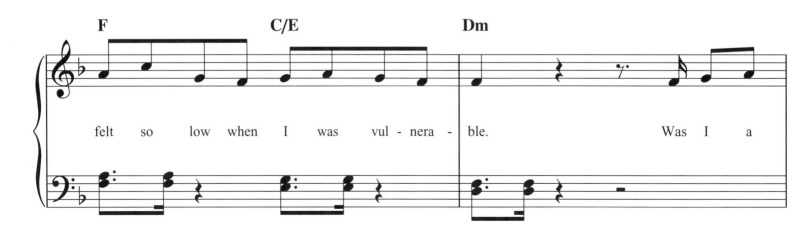

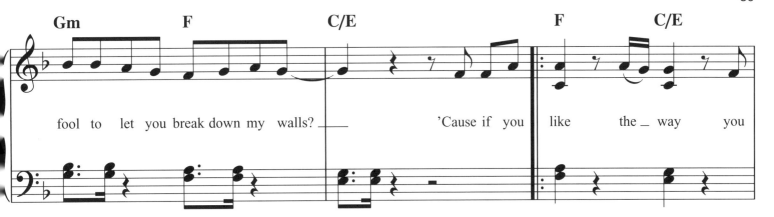

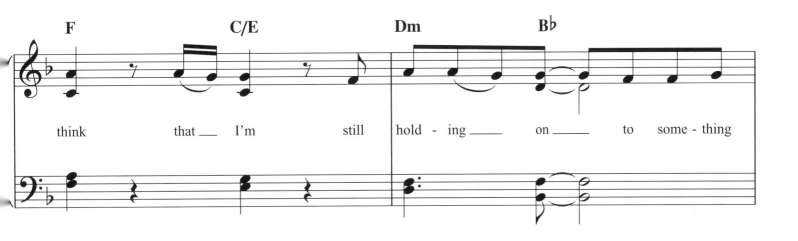

LUSH LIFE

Words and Music by MARKUS SEPEHRMANESH,
IMAN CONTA HULTEN, LINNEA SODAHL,
EMANUEL ARAHAMSSON, CHRISTOPH BAUSS
and FRIDOLIN WALCHER

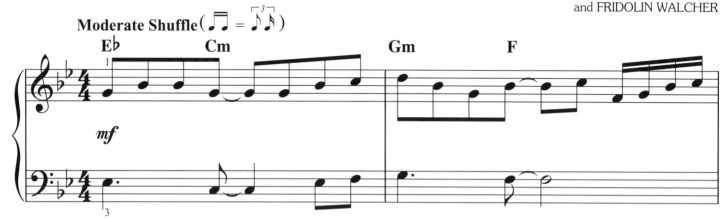

I live my day as

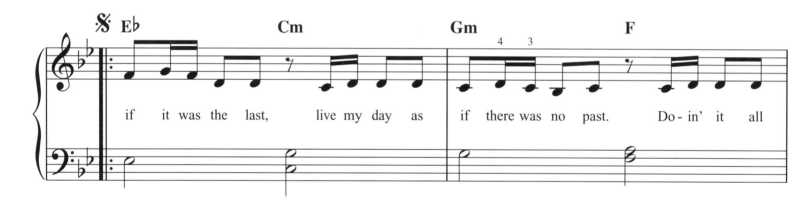

if it was the last, live my day as if there was no past. Do-in' it all

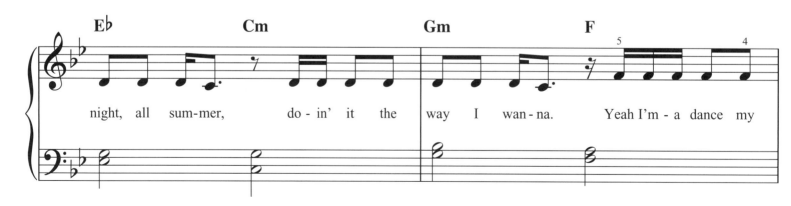

night, all sum-mer, do-in' it the way I wan-na. Yeah I'm-a dance my

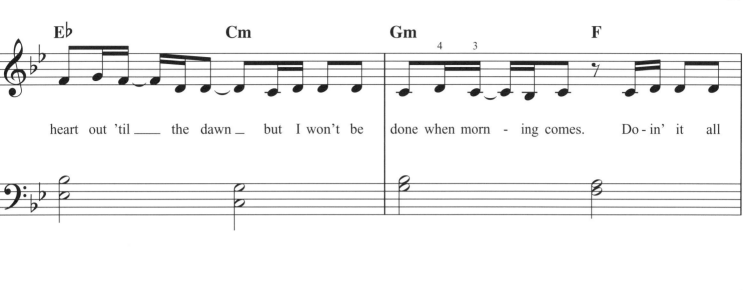

heart out 'til ___ the dawn ___ but I won't be done when morn - ing comes. Do - in' it all

night, all sum - mer, gon - na spend it like no oth - er. _____

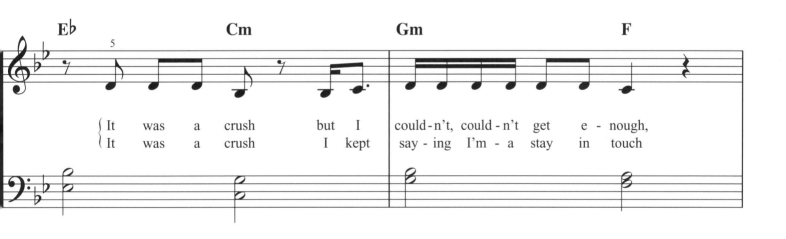

It was a crush but I could-n't, could-n't get e - nough,
It was a crush I kept say - ing I'm-a stay in touch

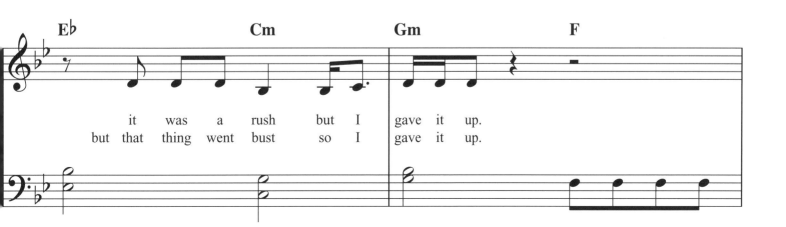

it was a rush but I gave it up.
but that thing went bust so I gave it up.

It was a crush now I might have went and said too much
No tricks, no bluff, I'm just bet-ter off with-out them cuffs, yeah, the

but that's all it was so I gave it up. I live my day as

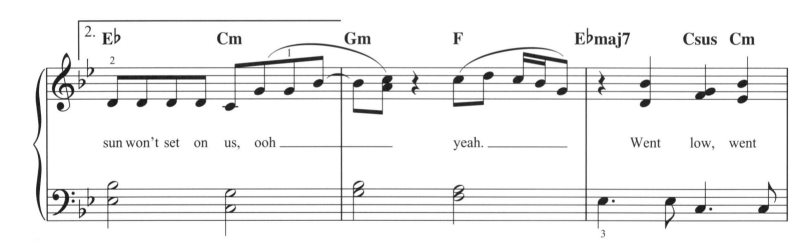

sun won't set on us, ooh _____ yeah. _____ Went low, went

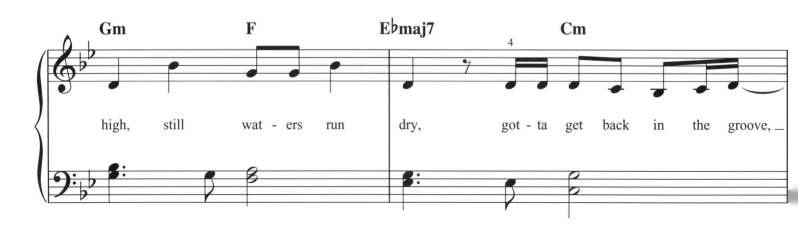

high, still wat-ers run dry, got-ta get back in the groove, _

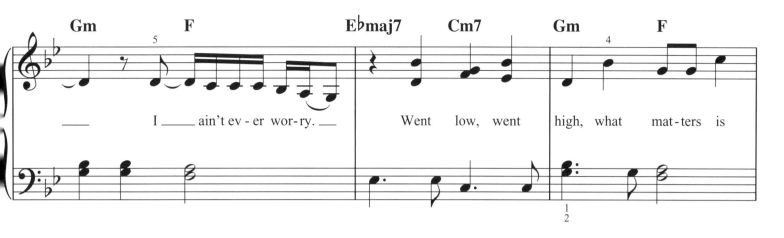

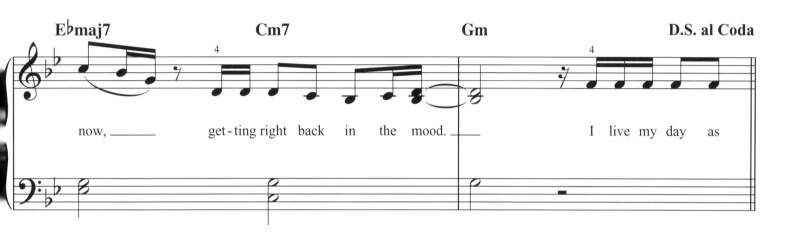

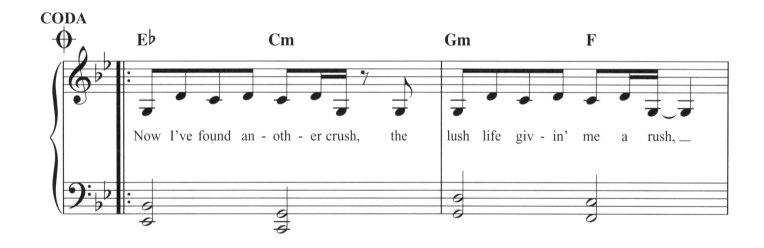

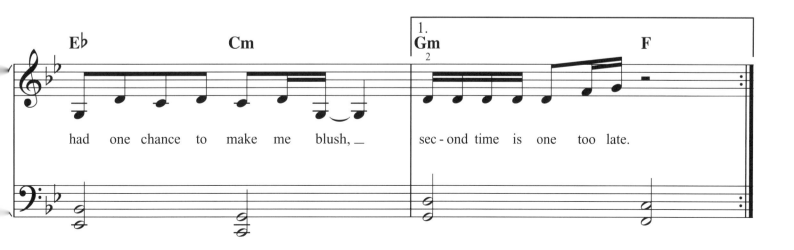

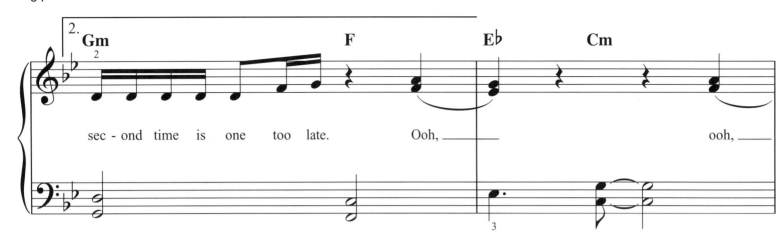

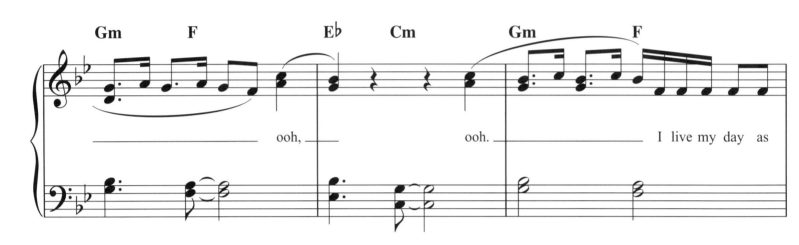

heart out 'til ___ the dawn, _ but I won't be | done when morn - ing comes. Do - in' it all

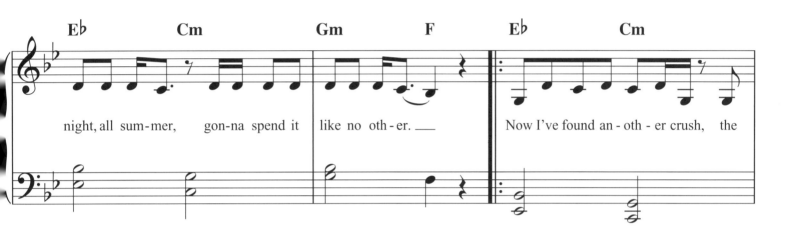

night, all sum-mer, gon-na spend it | like no oth-er. ___ | Now I've found an-oth-er crush, the

lush life giv-in' me a rush, _ | had one chance to make me blush, _

sec-ond time is one too late. | sec-ond time is one too late.

PERFECT STRANGERS

Words and Music by JOHN COOPER,
ALEX SMITH and JONAS BLUE

wast-ing your time, I'm not play-ing no games,
May-be we're help-ing each oth-er es-cape,

I see you. —
I'm with you. —

Who knows the se-cret to-mor-row will hold?

We don't real-ly need to know

'cause you're

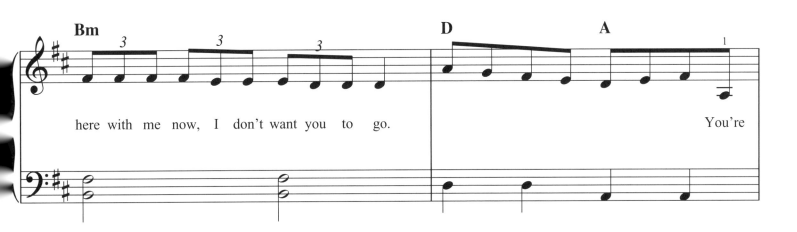

here with me now, I don't want you to go.

You're

here with me now, I don't want you to go. May - be we're per - fect stran - gers,

may - be it's not for - ev - er, may - be the light will change us, may - be we'll stay to - geth - er.

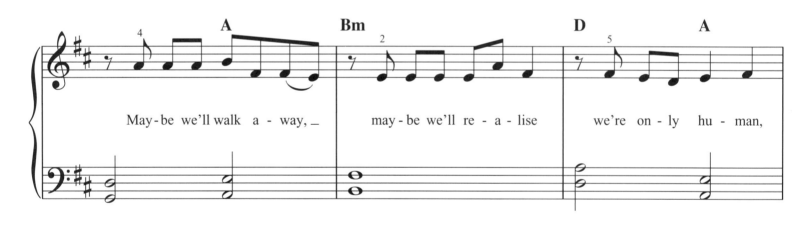

May - be we'll walk a - way, may - be we'll re - a - lise we're on - ly hu - man,

may - be we don't need no rea - son. May - be we're per - fect stran - gers, may - be it's not for - ev - er,

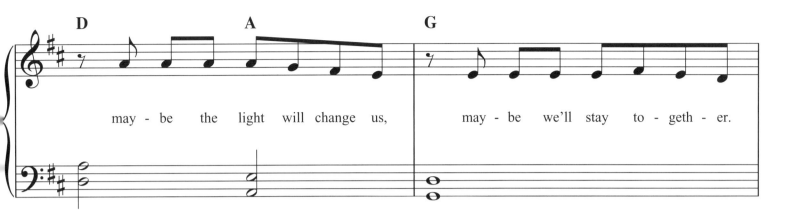

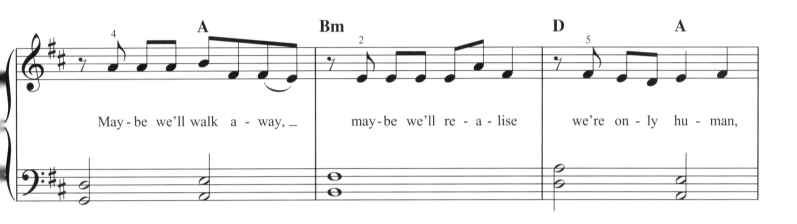

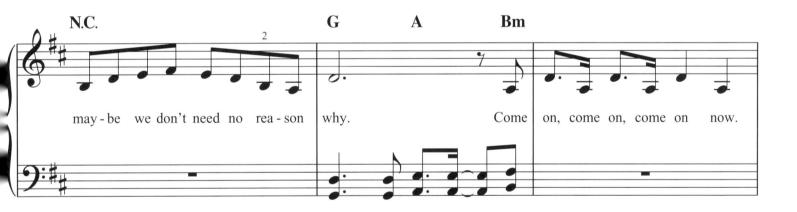

on, come on, come on now.

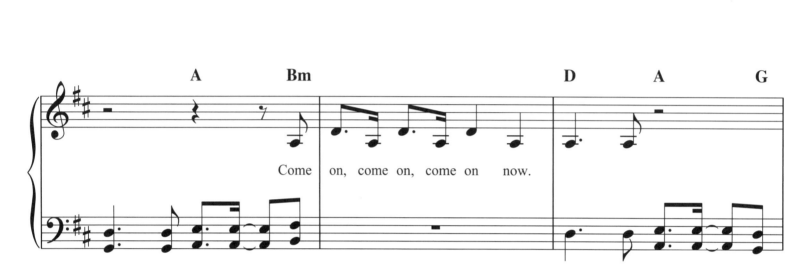

Come on, come on, come on now.

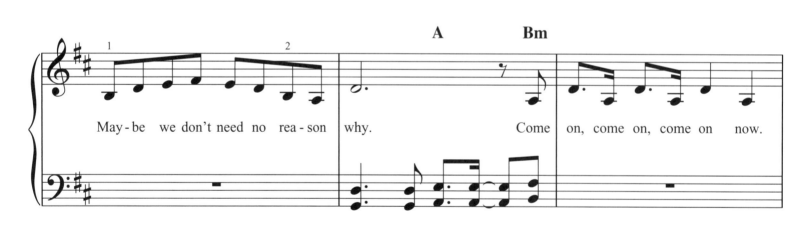

May-be we don't need no rea-son why. Come on, come on, come on now.

ROCKABYE

Words and Music by STEVE MAC, INA WROLDSEN,
JACK PATTERSON, SEAN PAUL HENRIQUES
and AMMAR MALIK

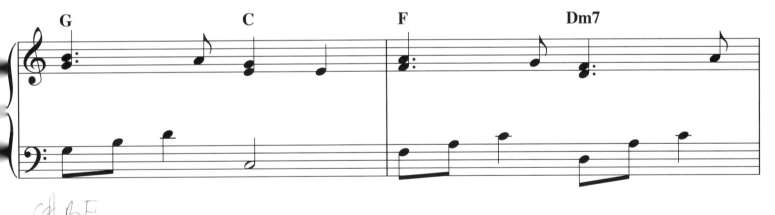

She works the nights, _____ by the wa - ter. She's gon-na stress, __

you. _____ She tells him, your life ___ ain't ___ gon' be noth-ing like

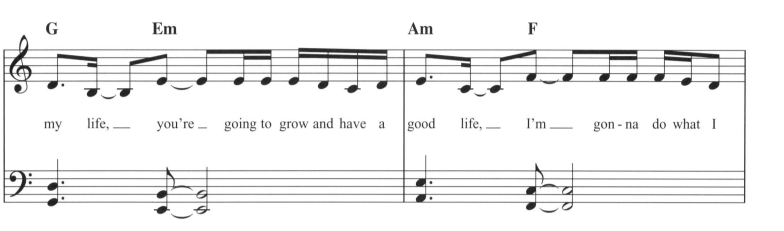

my life, ___ you're ___ going to grow and have a good life, ___ I'm ___ gon-na do what I

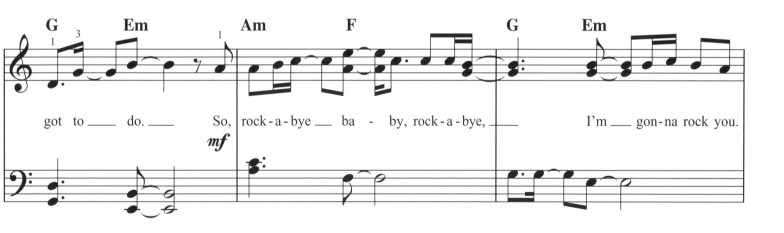

got to ___ do. ___ So, rock-a-bye ___ ba - by, rock-a-bye, ___ I'm ___ gon-na rock you.

Rock-a-bye ___ ba - by, don't you cry, ___ some - bod-y's got you.

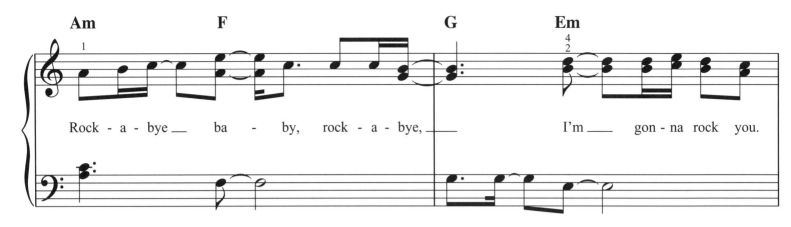

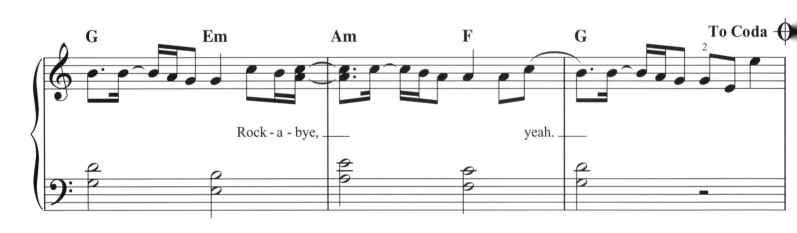

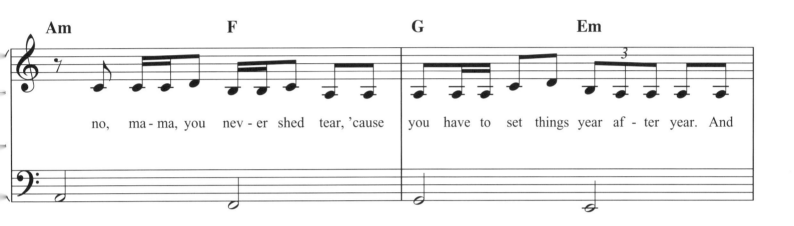

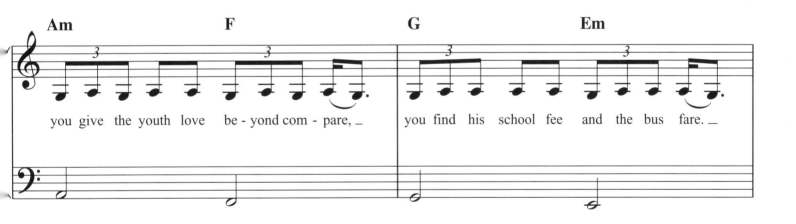

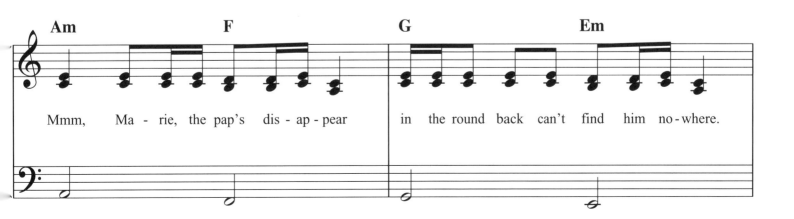

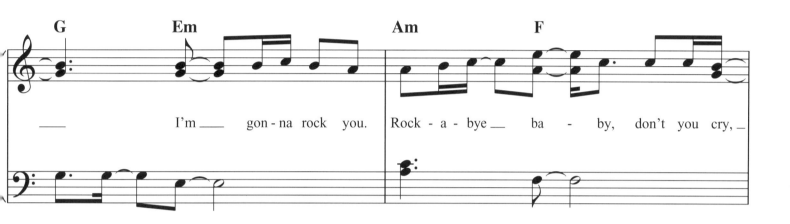

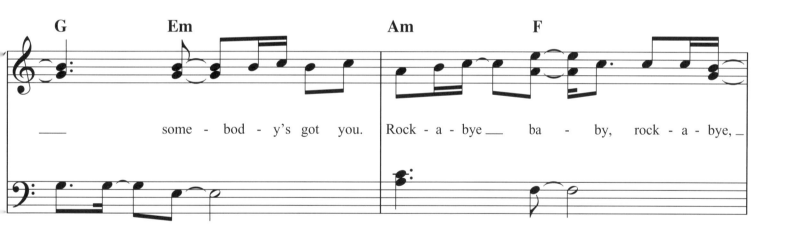

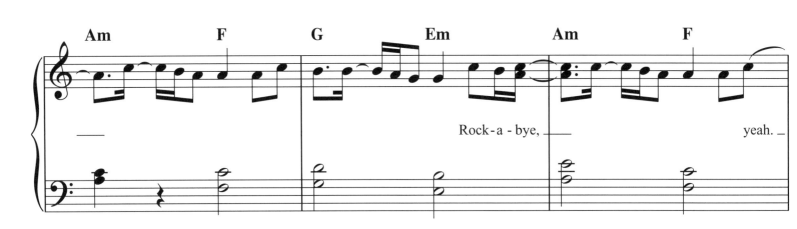

Rock-a - bye, _____ yeah. _

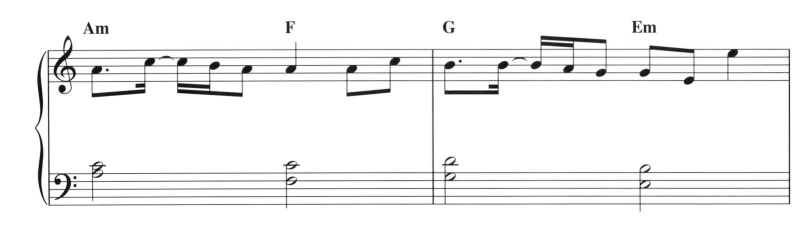

Now she got a six-year-old, try'n' to keep him warm, try'n' to keep out the

cold.   When he looks in her eyes, ___   he don't know he is safe, when she says; ___   she tells him

Rock - a - bye ___   ba - by, rock - a - bye, ___   I'm ___   gon-na rock you.

Rock - a - bye ___   ba - by, don't you   cry, ___   some - bod - y's got you.

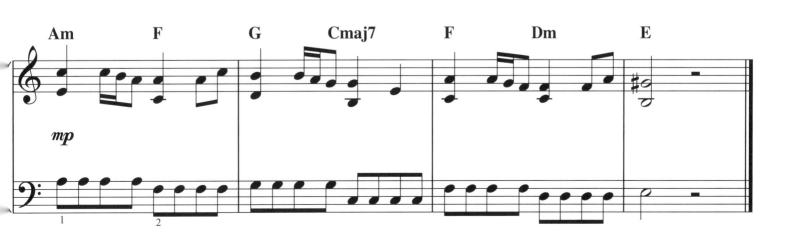

SAY YOU WON'T LET GO

Group C

Rt 1 Piano & Strgs
Rt 2 Octave horns.

Words and Music by STEVEN SOLOMON,
JAMES ARTHUR and NEIL ORMANDY

FGBbD

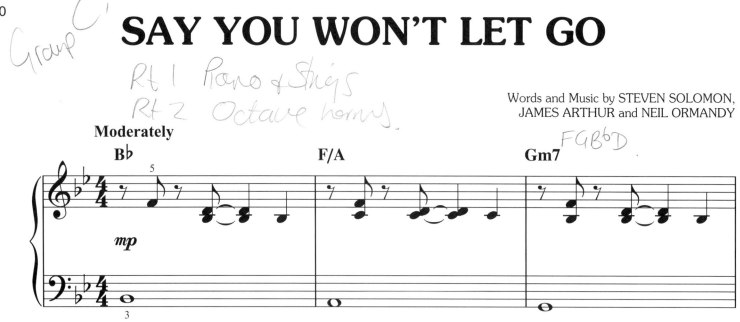

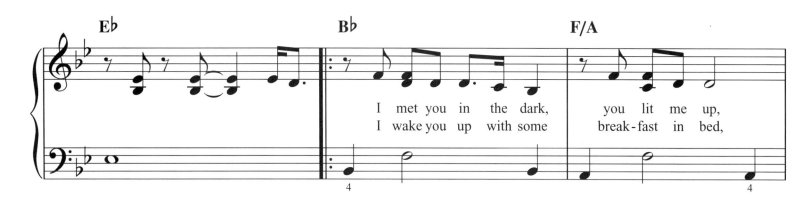

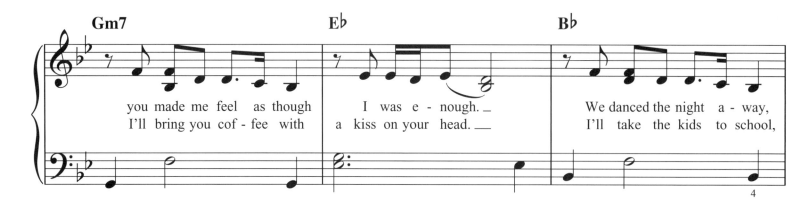

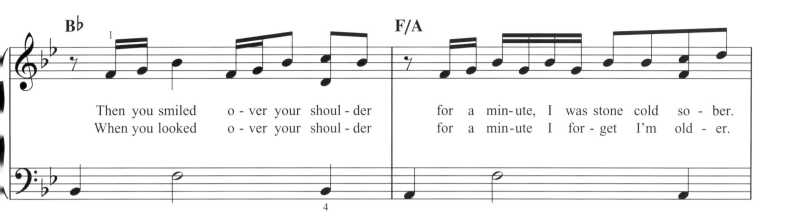

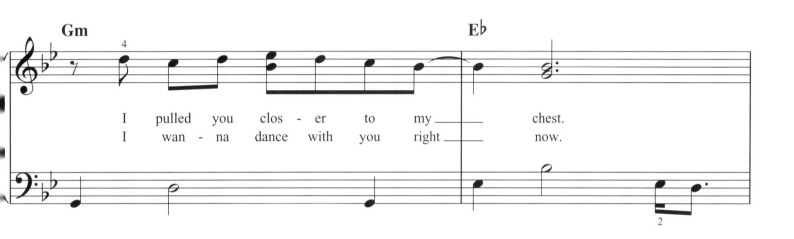

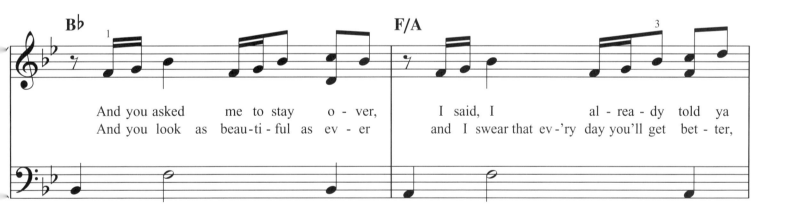

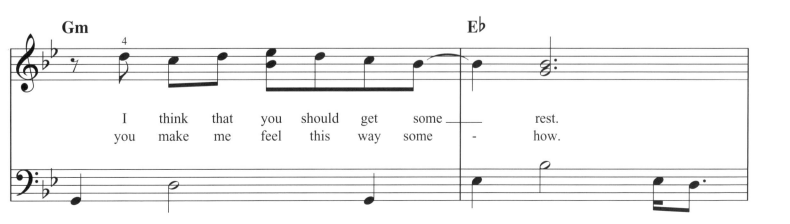

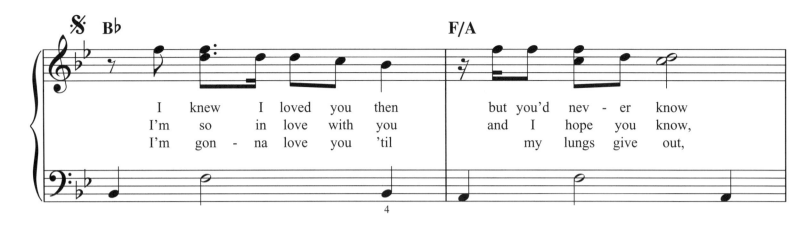

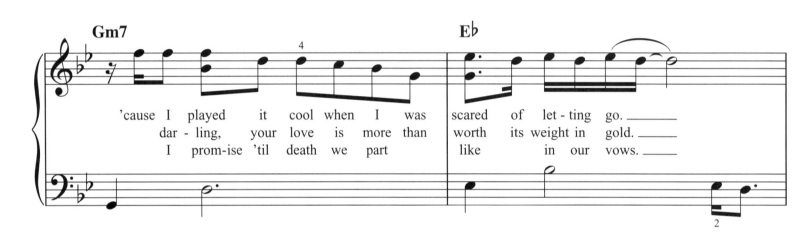

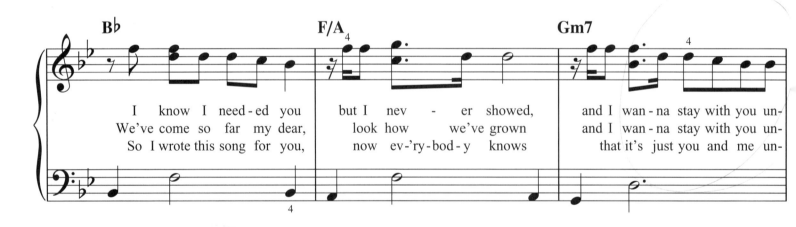

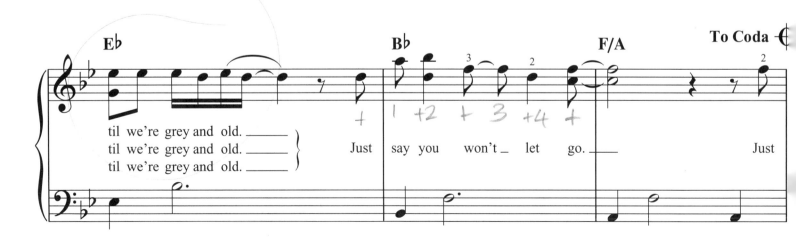

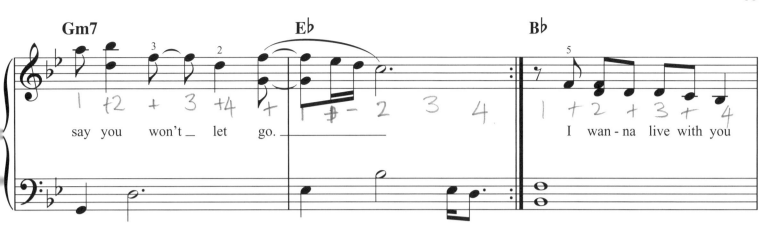

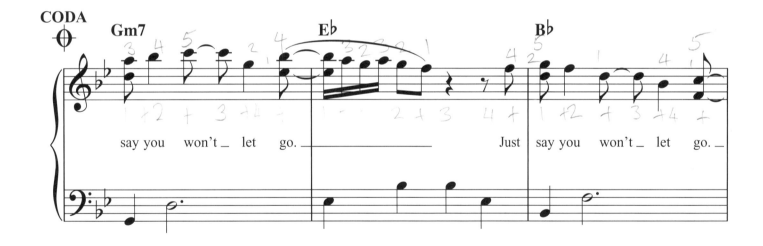

SIDE TO SIDE

Words and Music by ARIANA GRANDE,
ONIKA MARAJ, ALEXANDER KRONLUND,
MAX MARTIN, SAVAN KOTECHA and ILYA

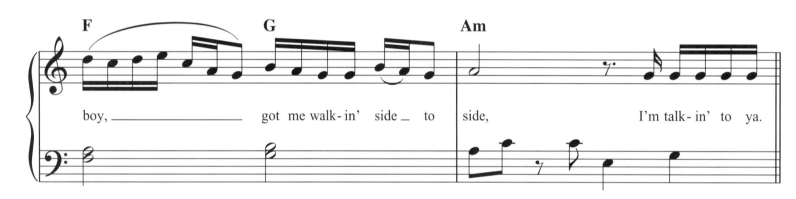

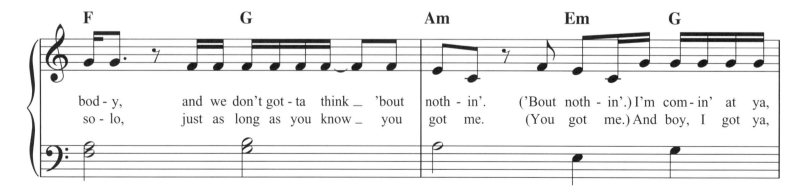

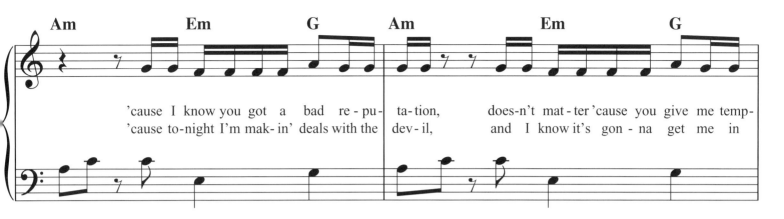

'cause I know you got a bad re-pu- ta-tion, does-n't mat-ter 'cause you give me temp-
'cause to-night I'm mak-in' deals with the dev-il, and I know it's gon-na get me in

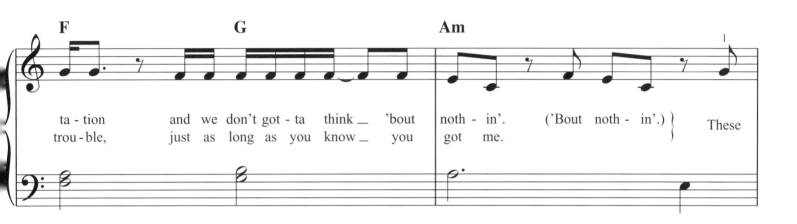

ta-tion and we don't got-ta think __ 'bout noth-in'. ('Bout noth-in'.) These
trou-ble, just as long as you know __ you got me.

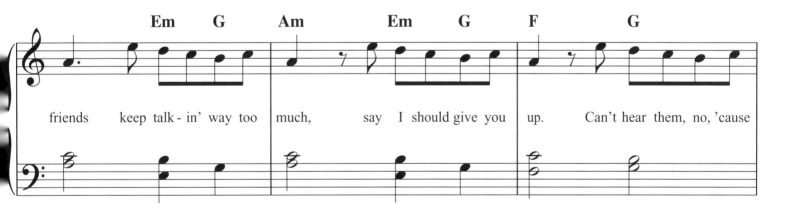

friends keep talk-in' way too much, say I should give you up. Can't hear them, no, 'cause

I... I've been there all night, I've been there all

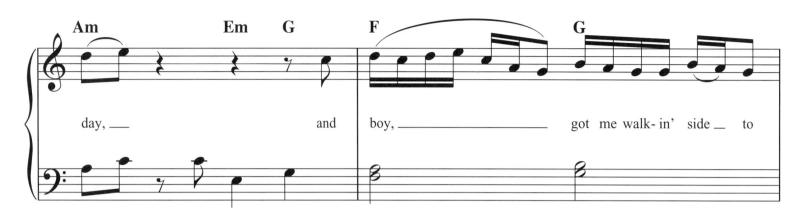

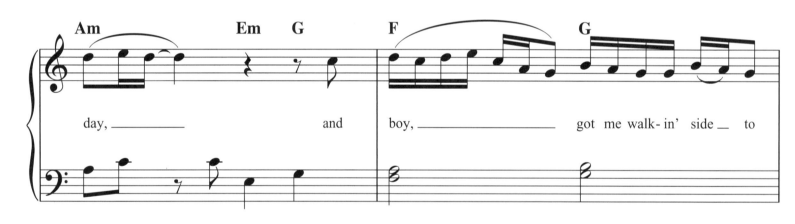

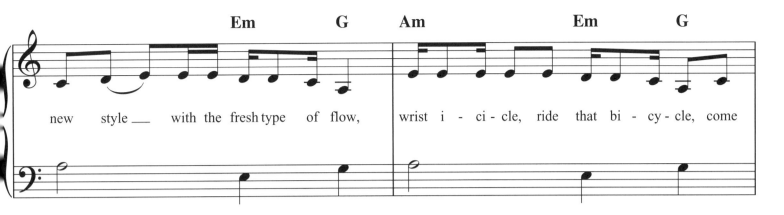

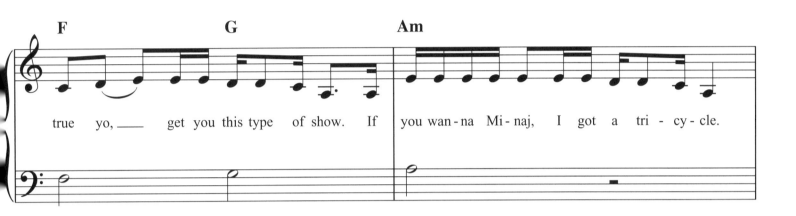

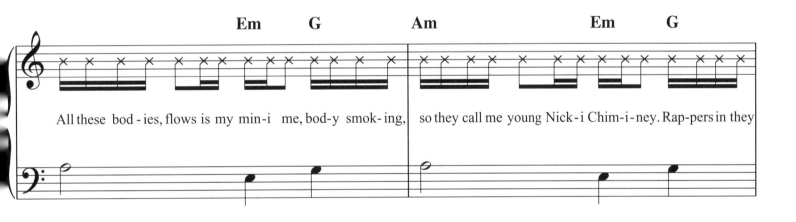

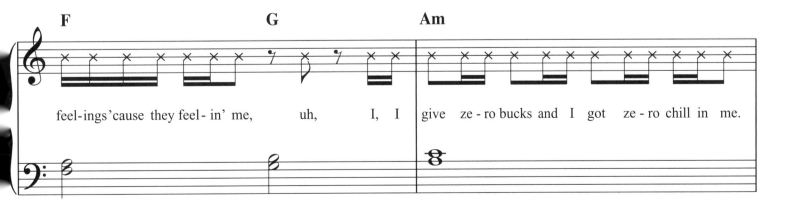

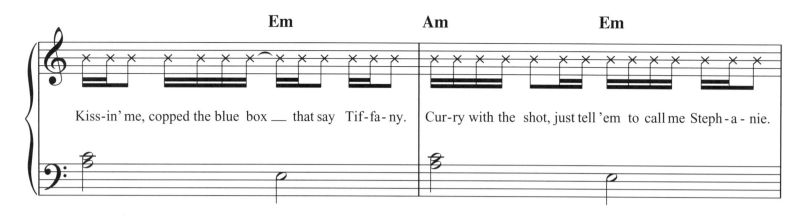

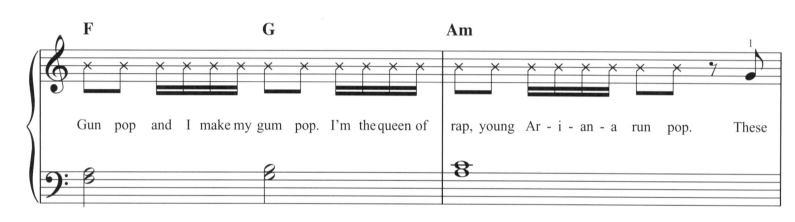

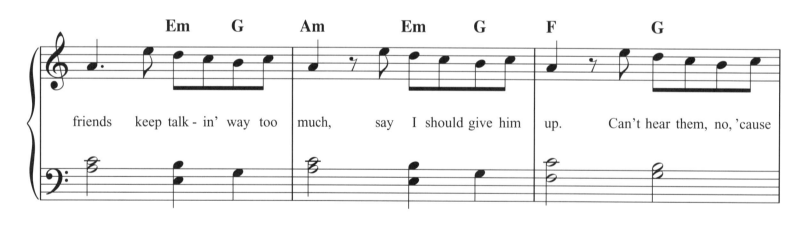

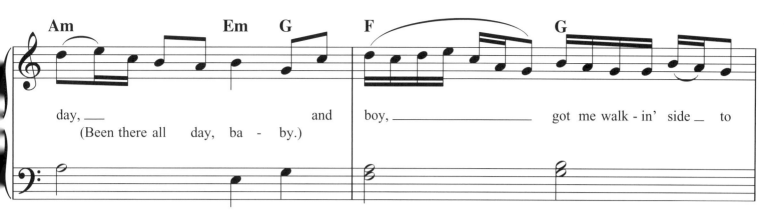

day, ___ (Been there all day, ba - by.) and boy, _____ got me walk - in' side ___ to

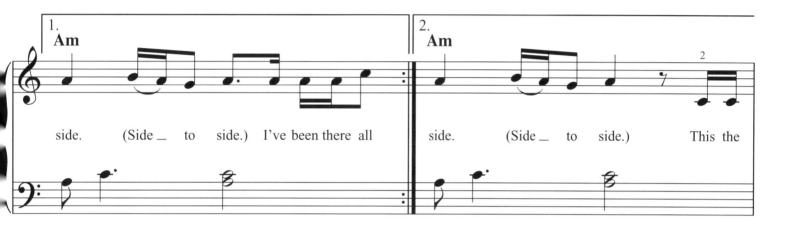

1.
side. (Side ___ to side.) I've been there all

2.
side. (Side ___ to side.) This the

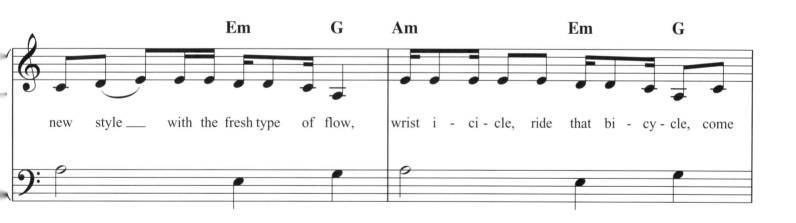

new style ___ with the fresh type of flow, wrist i - ci - cle, ride that bi - cy - cle, come

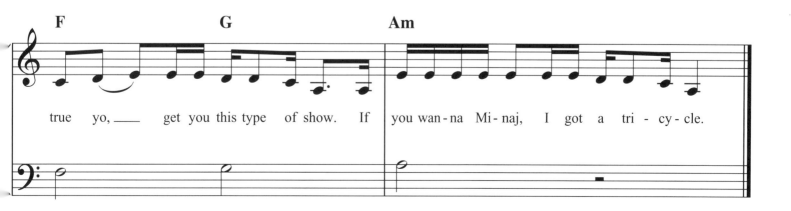

true yo, ___ get you this type of show. If you wan - na Mi - naj, I got a tri - cy - cle.

STARBOY

Words and Music by ABEL TESFAYE,
GUY-MANUEL DE HOMEM-CHRISTO, THOMAS BANGALTER,
HENRY WALTER, MARTIN McKINNEY and JASON QUENNEVILLE

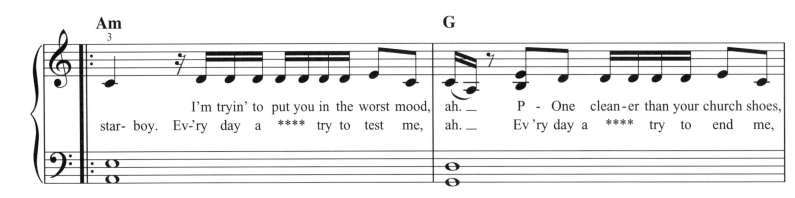

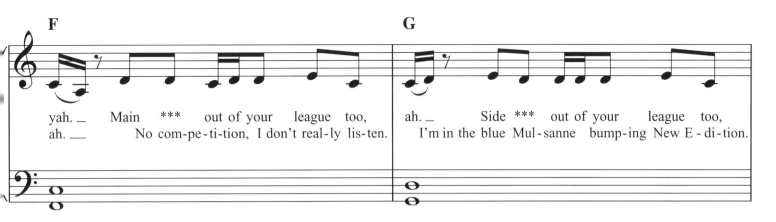

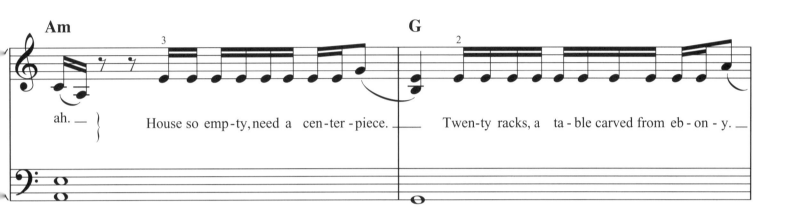

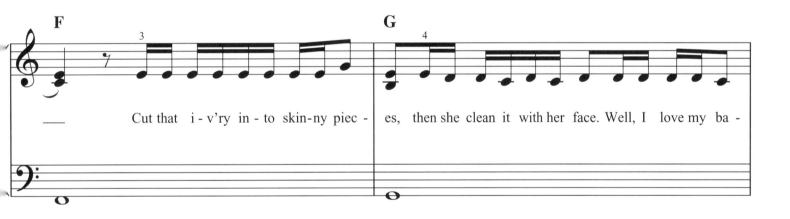

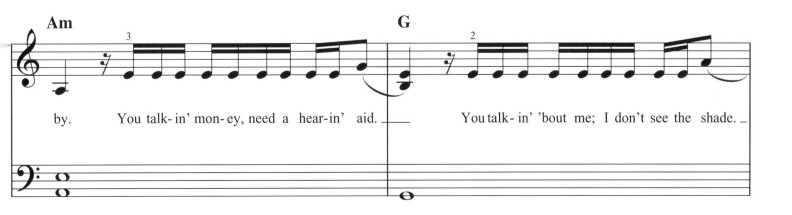

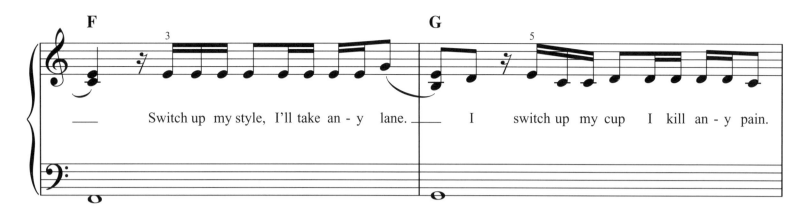

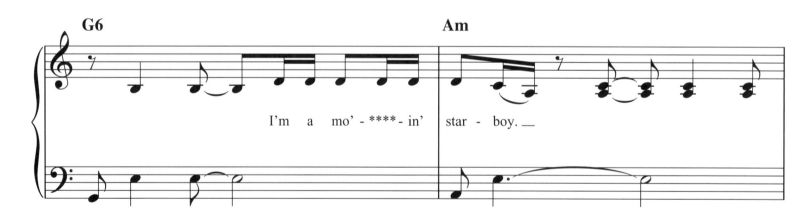

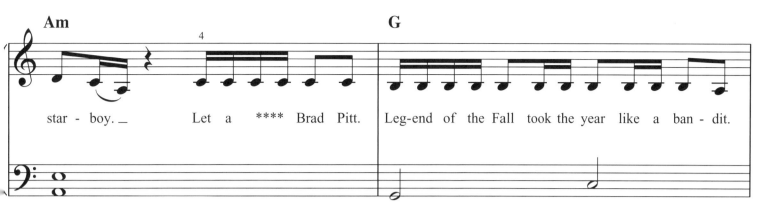

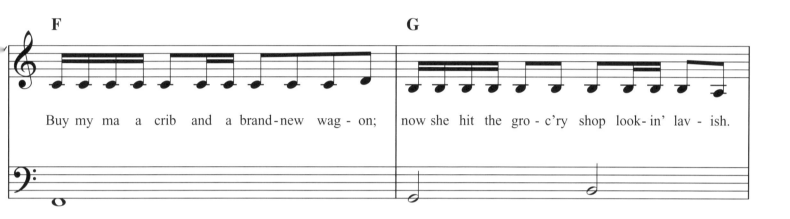

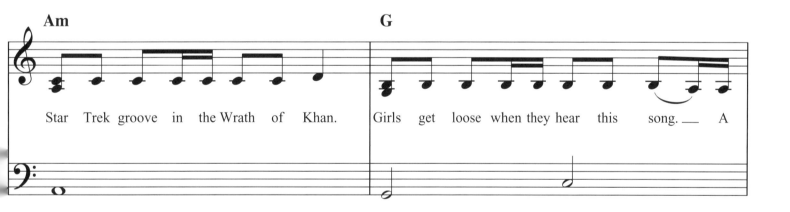

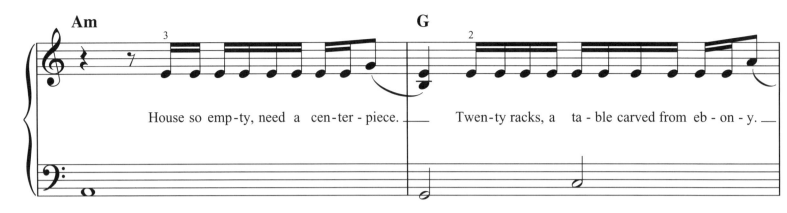

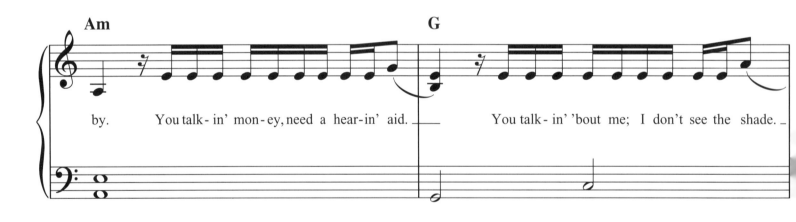

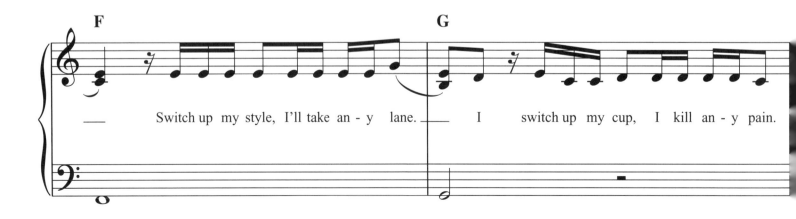

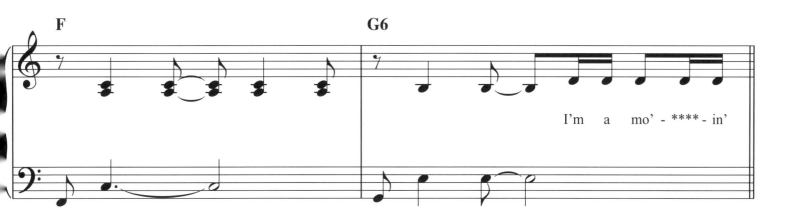

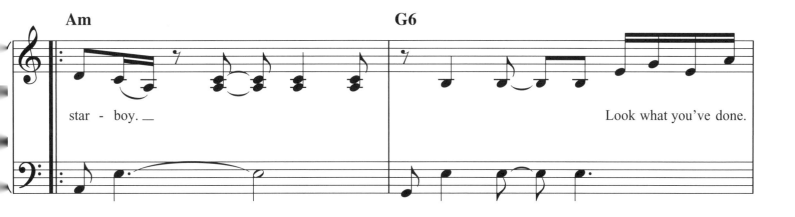

THIS TOWN

Words and Music by NIALL HORAN,
MICHAEL NEEDLE, DANIEL BRYER
and JAMIE SCOTT

Moderate Folk feel

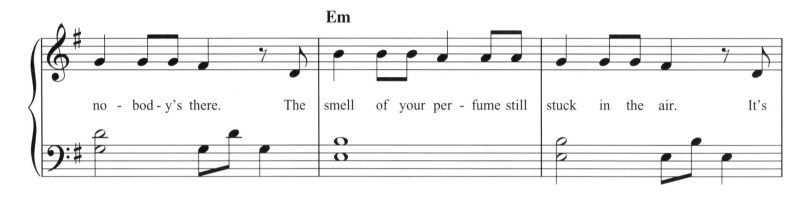

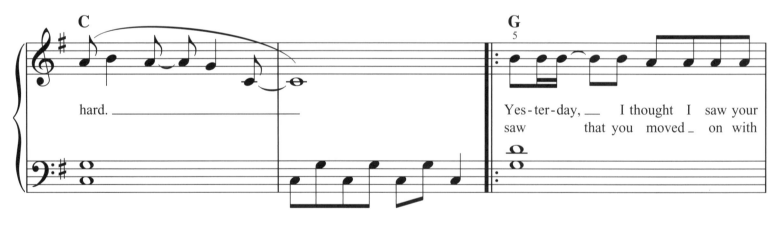

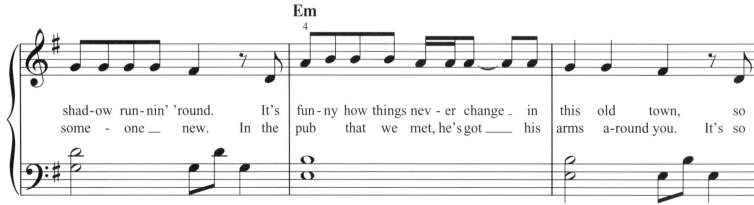

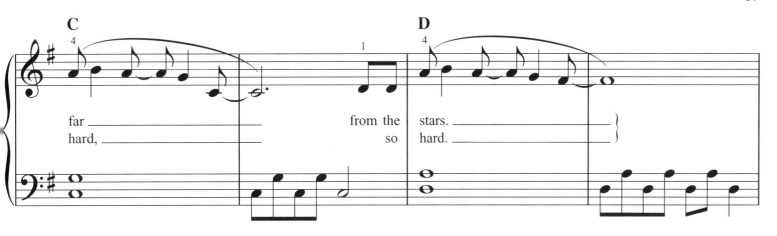

far _____
hard, _____ from the stars. _____
so hard. _____

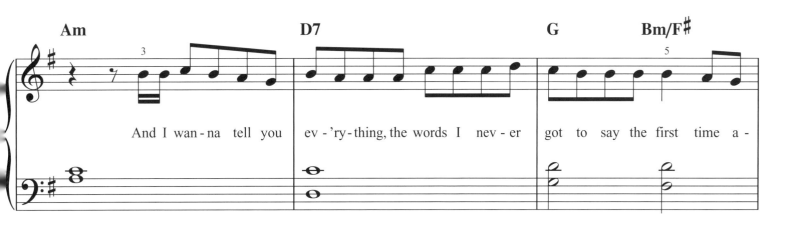

And I wan-na tell you ev-'ry-thing, the words I nev-er got to say the first time a-

round. __ And I re-mem-ber ev-'ry-thing from when we were __ the

chil-dren play-ing in this fair - ground. __ Wish I was there with you now. __

If the whole world was watch - ing, I'd still dance with you; drive

high - ways and by - ways to be there with you. O - ver and o - ver, the

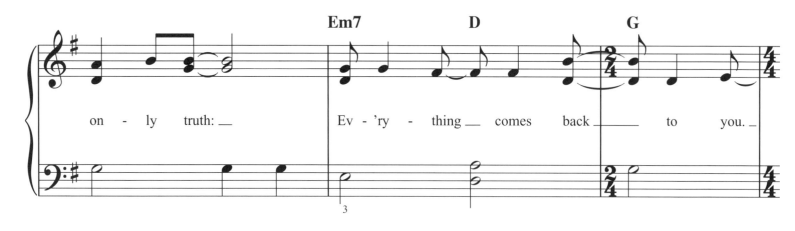

on - ly truth: __ Ev - 'ry - thing __ comes back __ to you. __

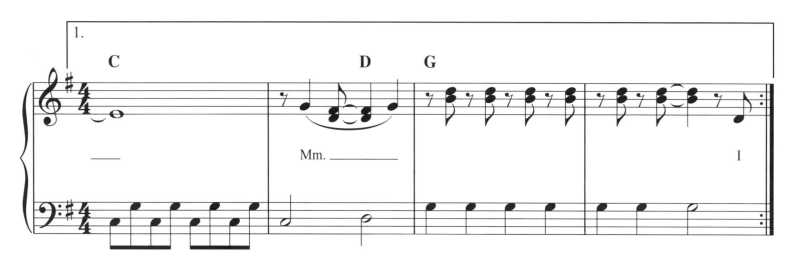

__ Mm. __ I

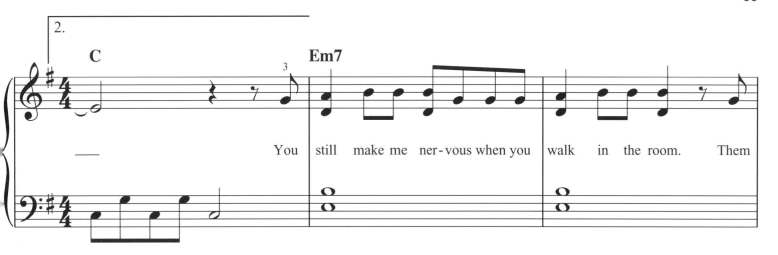

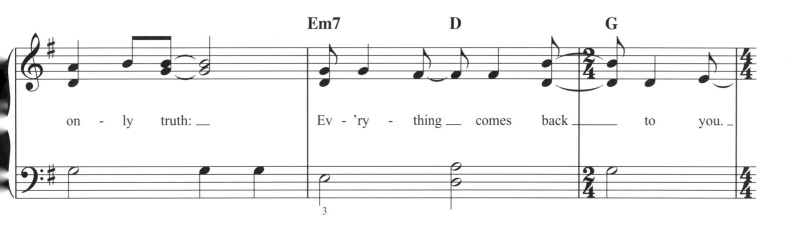

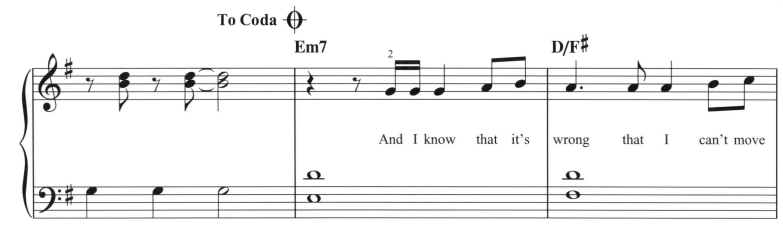

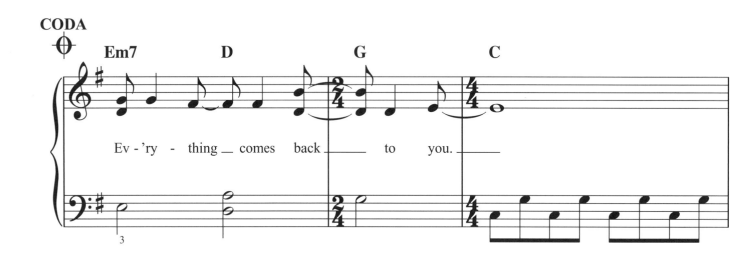

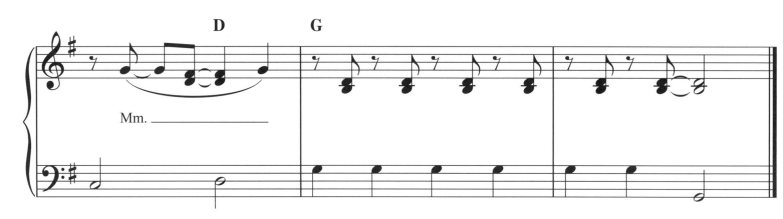

TREAT YOU BETTER

Words and Music by SHAWN MENDES,
SCOTT HARRIS and TEDDY GEIGER

Moderately, in 2

I won't lie to you.
I'll stop time for you

I know he's just not right
the sec - ond you say you'd like me to.

And you can tell me if I'm off, but I
I just wan - na give you the

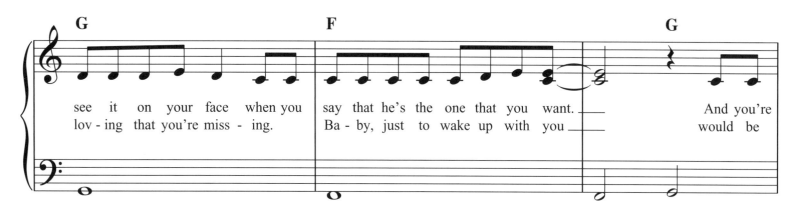

see it on your face when you / say that he's the one that you want.___ And you're
lov - ing that you're miss - ing. / Ba - by, just to wake up with you ___ would be

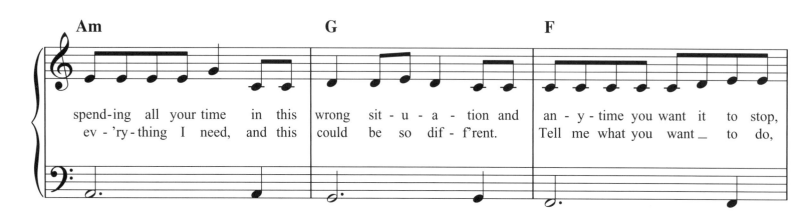

spend-ing all your time in this / wrong sit - u - a - tion and / an - y - time you want it to stop,
ev - 'ry-thing I need, and this / could be so dif - f'rent. / Tell me what you want ___ to do,

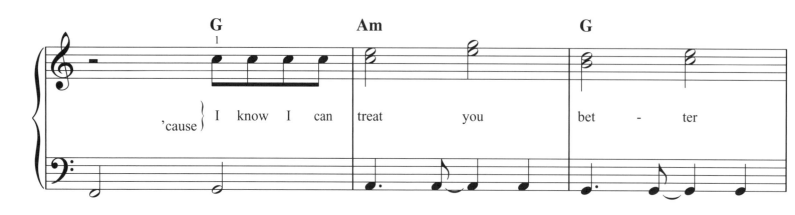

'cause I know I can treat you bet - ter

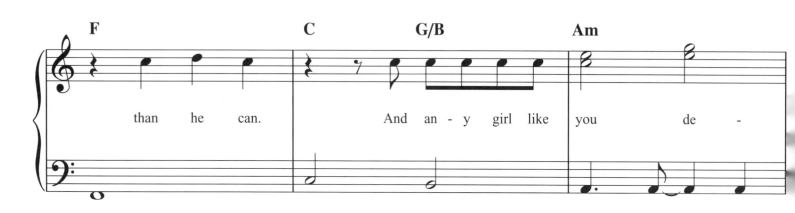

than he can. And an - y girl like you de -

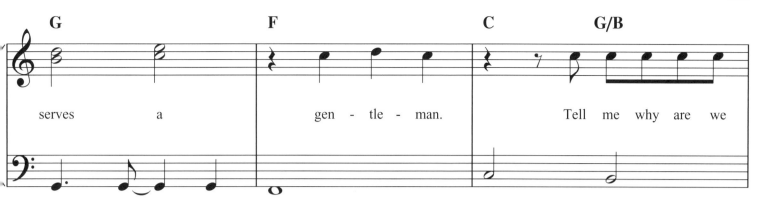

serves a gen - tle - man. Tell me why are we

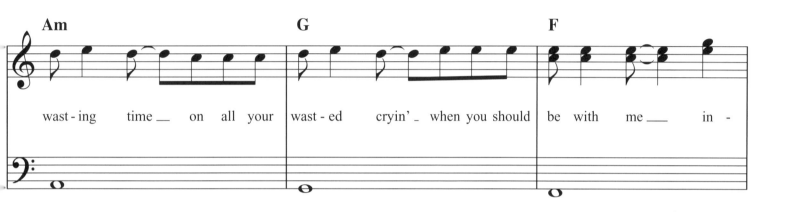

wast - ing time __ on all your wast - ed cryin' __ when you should be with me __ in -

stead? I know I can treat you bet - ter,

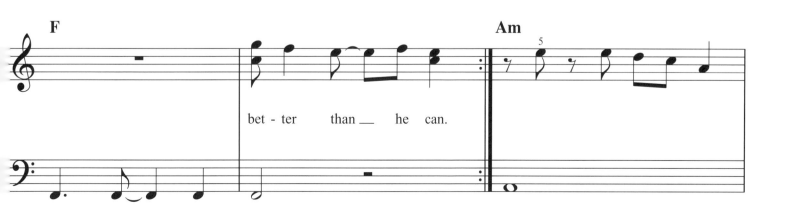

bet - ter than __ he can.

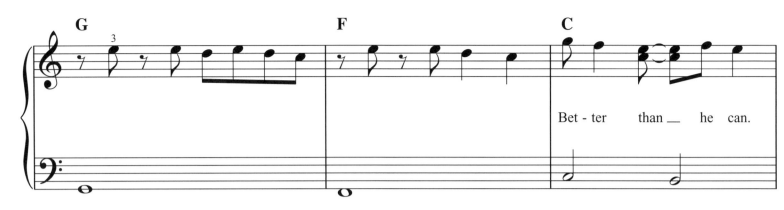

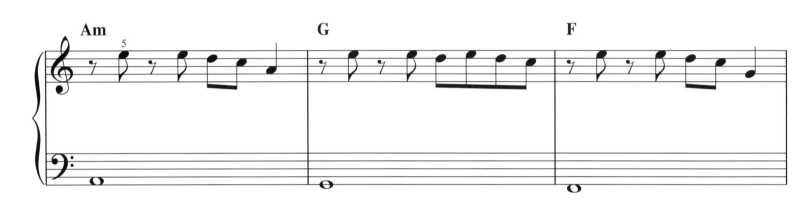

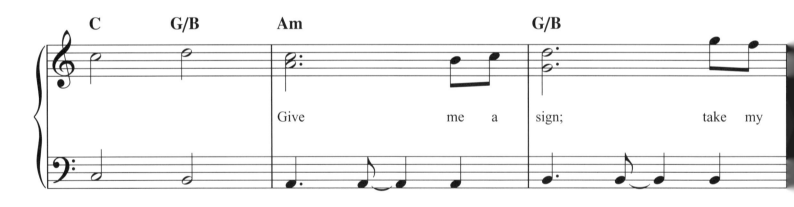

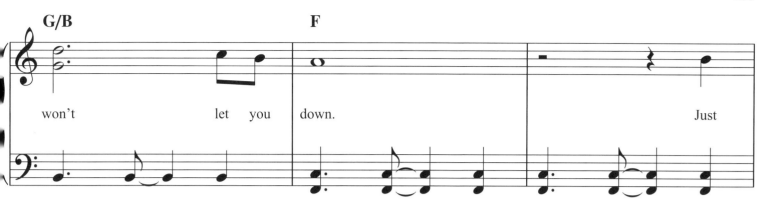

won't let you down. Just

know that you don't have to do this a-

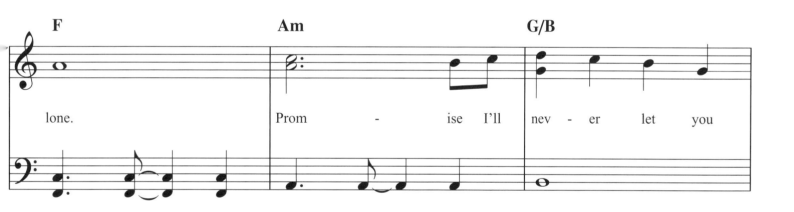

lone. Prom - ise I'll nev - er let you

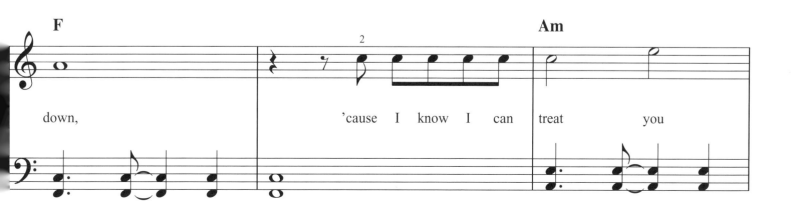

down, 'cause I know I can treat you

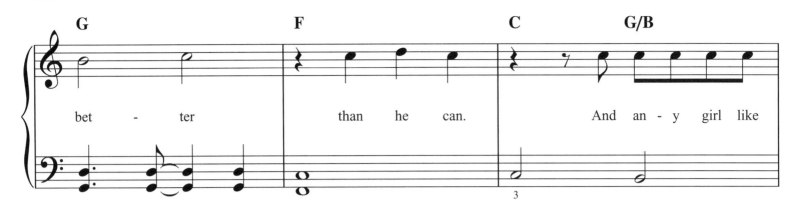

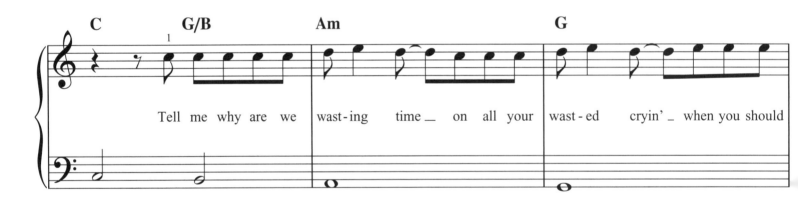

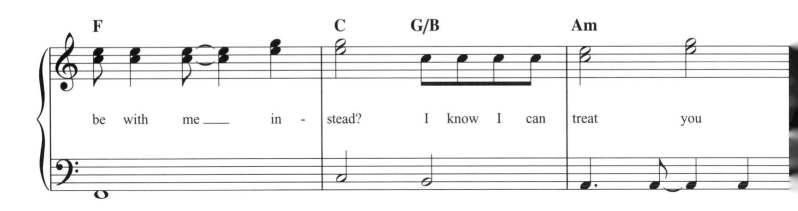

better, better than __ he can.

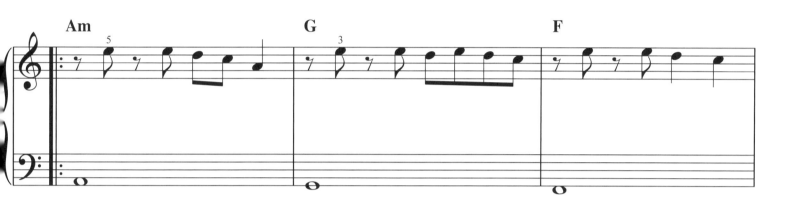

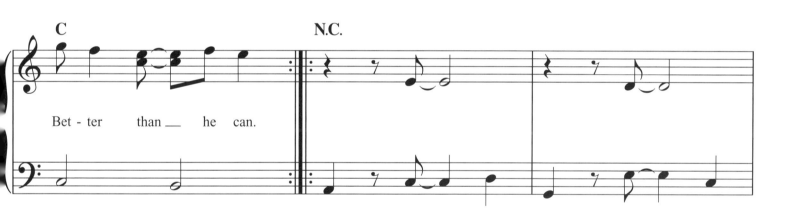

Better than __ he can.

24K MAGIC

Words and Music by BRUNO MARS,
PHILIP LAWRENCE and CHRIS BROWN

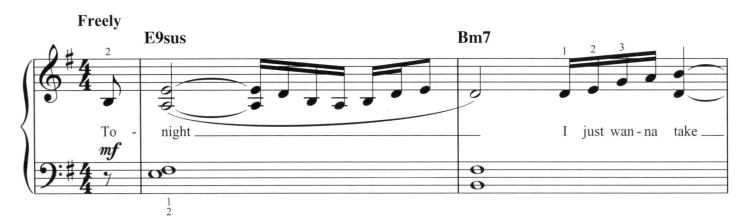

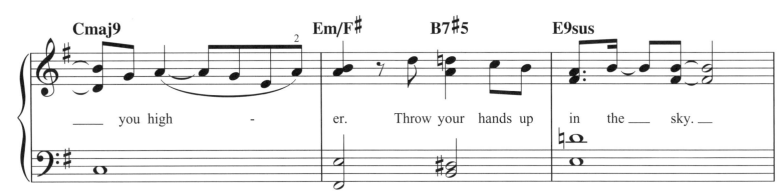

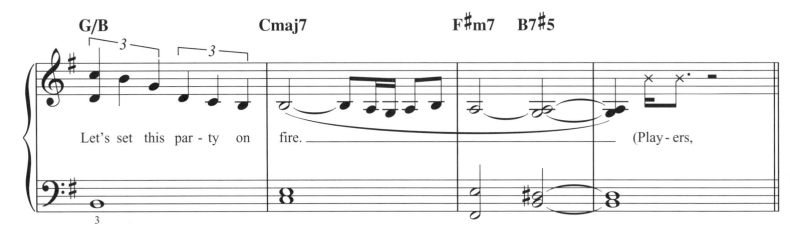

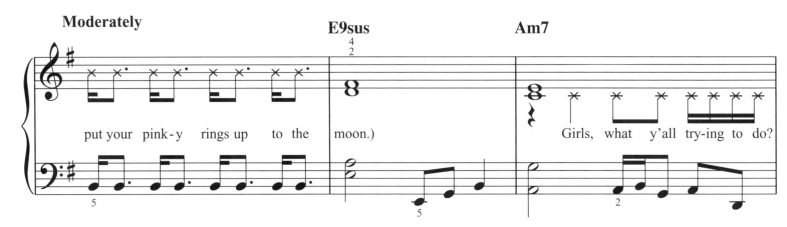

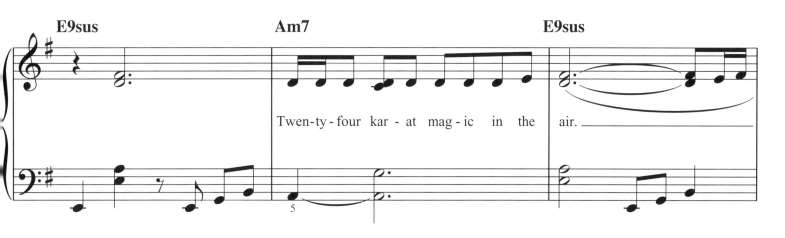

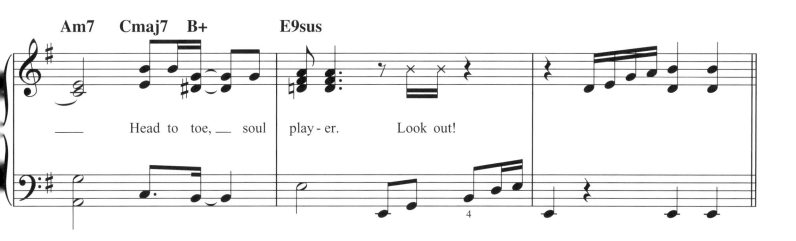

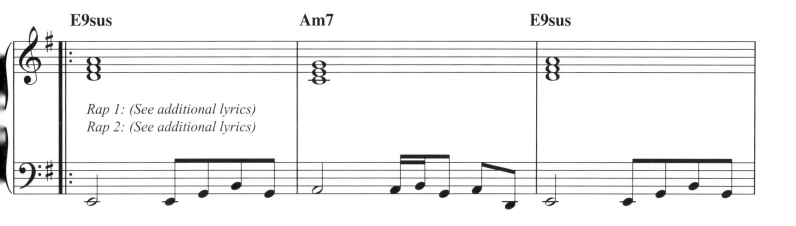

Rap 1: (See additional lyrics)
Rap 2: (See additional lyrics)

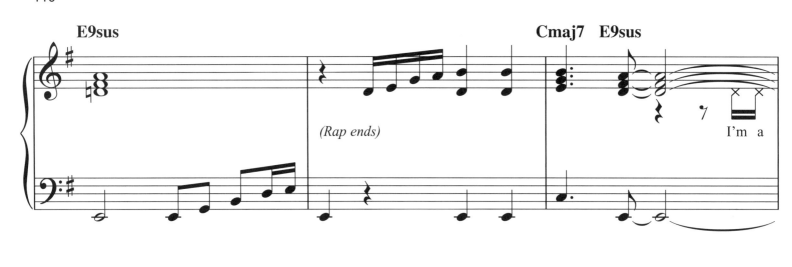

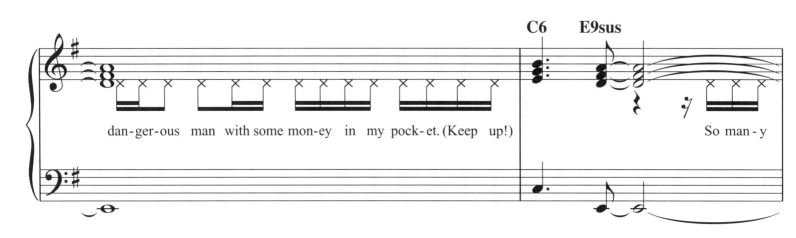

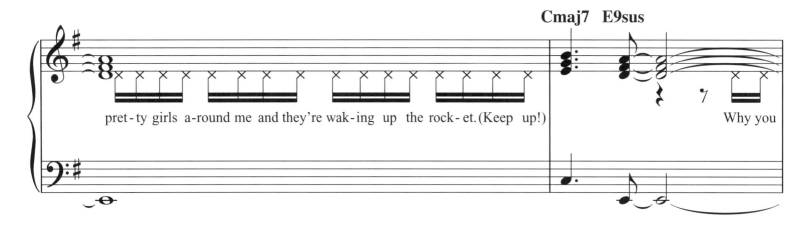

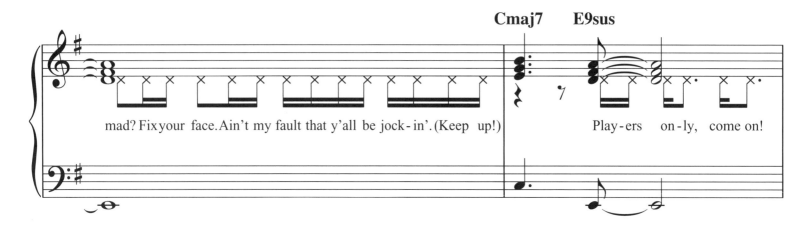

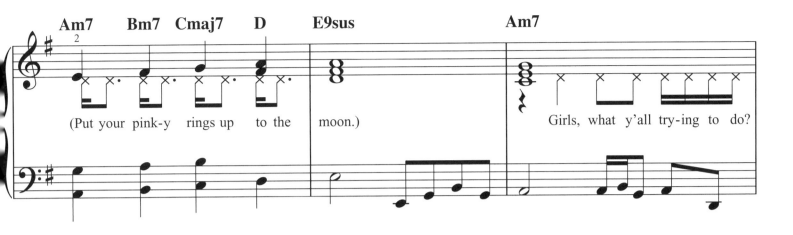

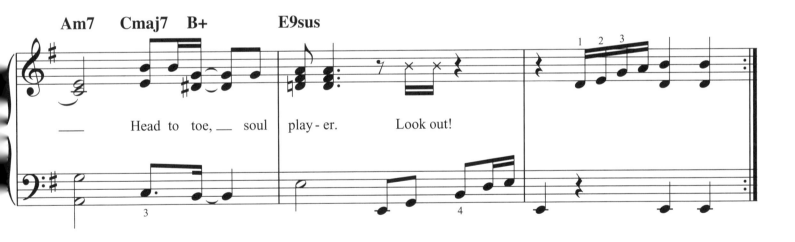

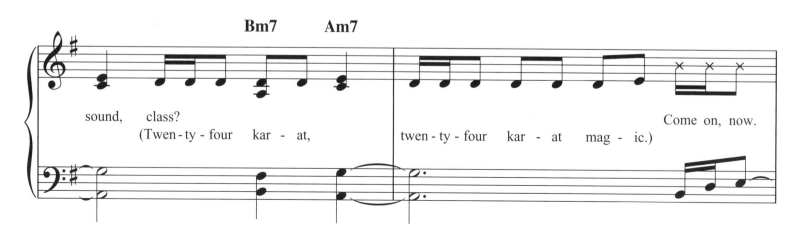

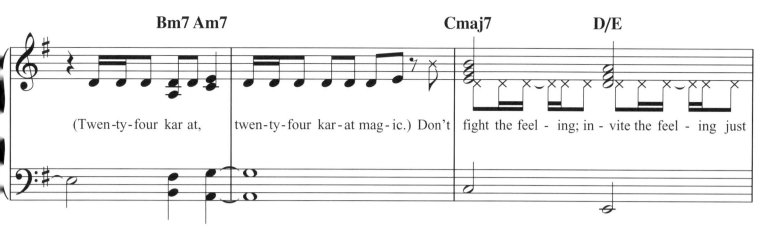

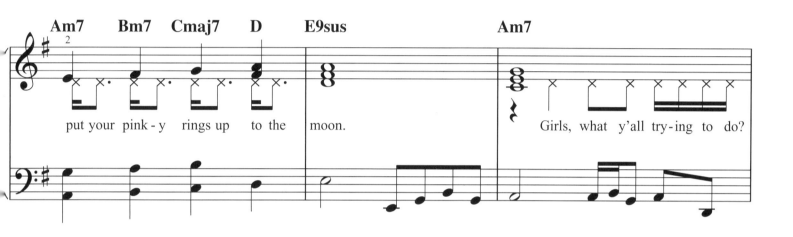

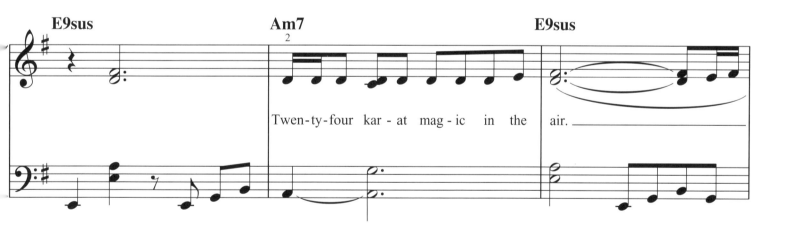

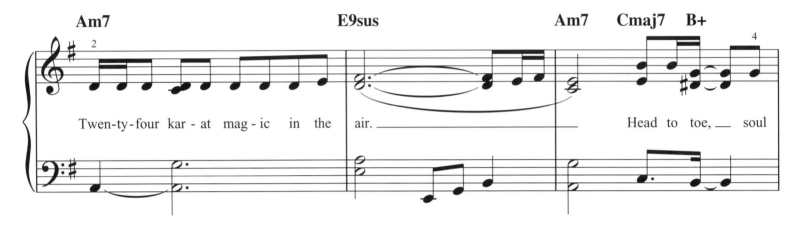

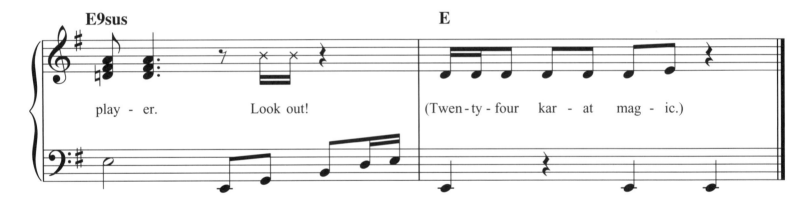

Additional Lyrics

Rap 1: Pop, pop, it's show time (show time) show time (show time).
Guess who's back again?
Oh, they don't know? (Go on, tell 'em.)
They don't know? (Go on, tell 'em.)
I bet they know as soon as we walk in.
(Showin' up) wearin' Cuban links, (yeah) designer minks (yeah).
Inglewood's finest shoes (whoop, whoop).
Don't look too hard; might hurt yourself.
Known to give the color red the blues.

Rap 2: Second verse for the hustlers, (hustlers) gangsters (gangsters).
Bad bitches and your ugly-ass friends.
Can I preach? (Uh-oh.) Can I preach? (Uh-oh.)
I gotta show 'em how a pimp get it in.
First, take your sip (sip) do your dip (dip).
Spend your money like money ain't shit.
(Ooh, ooh, we too fresh.)
Got to blame it on Jesus (#blessed).
They ain't ready for me.

WORK FROM HOME

Words and Music by DALLAS KOEHLKE,
JOSHUA COLEMAN, ALEXANDER IZQUIERDO,
TYRONE WILLIAM GRIFFIN JR., BRIAN LEE
and JUDE DEMOREST

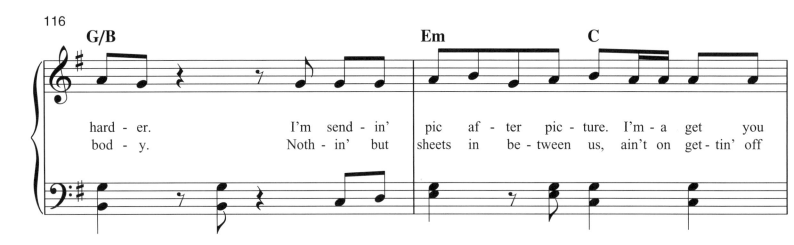

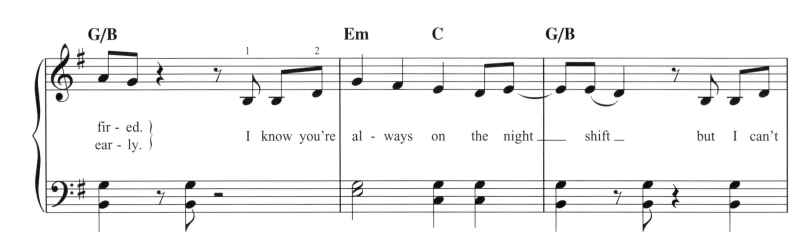

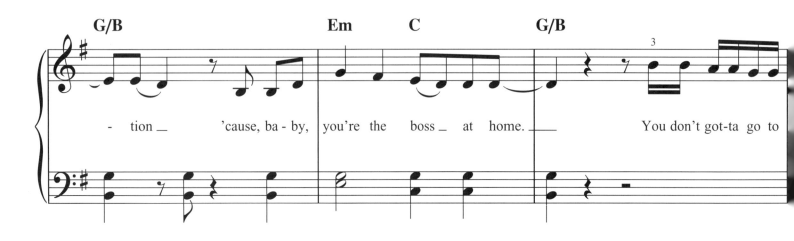

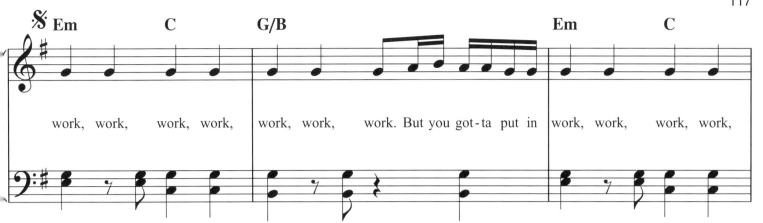

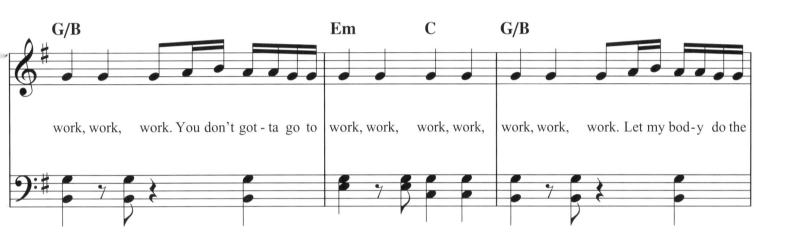

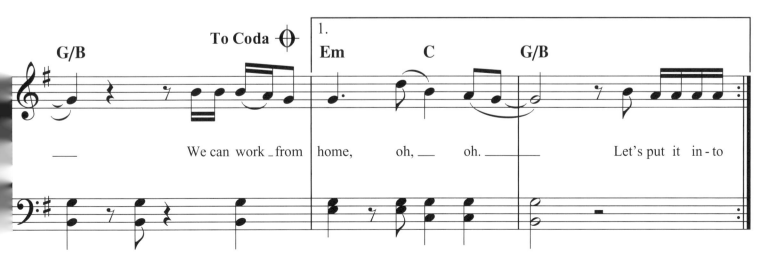

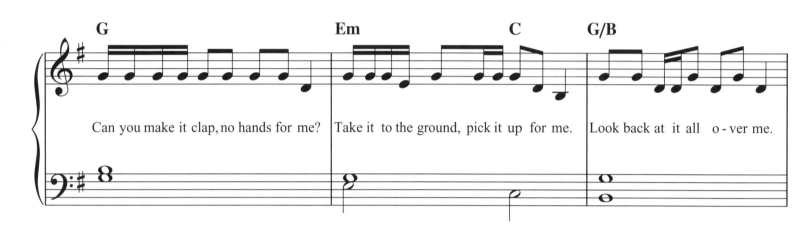

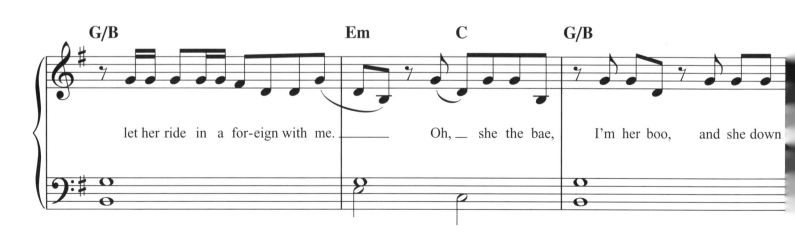

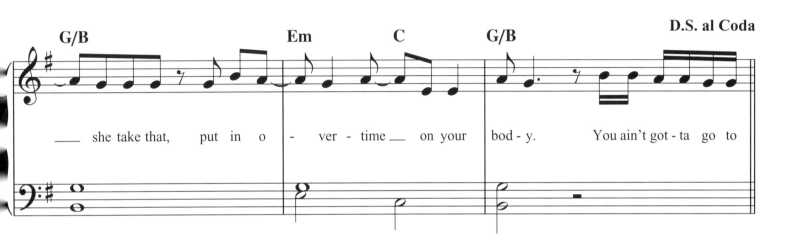